World Timbers
VOLUME THREE

WORLD TIMBERS

VOLUME THREE

ASIA & AUSTRALIA & NEW ZEALAND

Compiled and edited by

B. J. RENDLE

LONDON: ERNEST BENN LIMITED

UNIVERSITY OF TORONTO PRESS

First published in this form 1970
by Ernest Benn Limited
Bouverie House, Fleet Street, London, EC4
Published in Canada and United States by
University of Toronto Press
0-8020-1718-5

© Ernest Benn Limited 1970
Printed in Great Britain
ISBN 0-510-48003-9

Contents

Introduction *page 7*

Asian Timbers

[*continued on page 6*]

Contents [continued from page 5]

Introduction

A feature of the journal *Wood*, since it commenced publication in 1936, has been the two series of colour plates of timbers accompanied by technical information on their properties and uses. The first series, under the name WOOD SPECIMENS, covered the years 1936–1960; this was followed by the series WORLD TIMBERS. A selection of one hundred of the WOOD SPECIMENS was reproduced in book form in 1949[1] and a second volume appeared in 1957[2]. A disadvantage of these volumes, which are now out of print, was the haphazard arrangement of the timbers. The present work is based on plates selected from both series (WOOD SPECIMENS and WORLD TIMBERS) in a more systematic arrangement with the technical information revised where necessary.

The first two volumes of WORLD TIMBERS dealt with the more important species of Europe and Africa (Volume 1) and North and South America, Central America and the West Indies (Volume 2). Volume 3 covers Asia, Australia and New Zealand. The selection of timbers for inclusion in a book of this kind is bound to be somewhat arbitrary. Many species of economic significance in their countries of origin have had to be omitted while others have been included because they are more widely known or are considered more representative.

The Colour Plates
Most of the plates in this volume originally appeared in *Wood* between 1936 and 1970. Ten are new and are now published for the first time. Thanks are due to those timber importers and others who kindly supplied the specimens used to prepare the plates.
Care has been taken to ensure that the specimens are representative of the timbers concerned. However, anyone with a knowledge of wood is well aware of the limitations of a single specimen or a single illustration. Allowance must be made for the normal variations in colour, grain and texture, which are so characteristic of wood, as also the differences in appearance due to the method of converting a log (by sawing through-and-through, or by quartering, rotary peeling, slicing, etc.) and the different types of decorative figure that are found in abnormal logs.
Some indication of the variation that is to be expected and the changes in colour that occur with the passage of time is given in the description accompanying each plate. It is advisable, however, when choosing wood for high-class decorative work —whether solid timber or veneer—to examine and select material from the merchant's actual stocks. Small samples may be misleading.

The Technical Descriptions
The technical information accompanying the plates is presented in a form designed to appeal to those who are interested in timber but are not specialists in wood technology. The publishers believe that it will be particularly useful to architects and their clients and those members of the timber trade, the timber-using industries and the general public who do not have access to a representative collection of timber specimens and a library of standard reference books on timber.

---

[1] Wood Specimens—100 Reproductions in Colour. The Nema Press, London, 1949.
[2] A Second Collection of Wood Specimens—100 Reproductions in Colour. The Tothill Press Ltd., London, 1957.

Each timber is described in such detail as its importance seems to warrant. The aim is to indicate its outstanding characteristics and to bring out the practical significance of the information presented.

In selecting a timber for a particular purpose some knowledge of the supply position is essential. The section headed *Distribution and supplies* gives the geographical distribution in broad terms, emphasising the principal sources of supply, with some indication of the quantity and sizes available and whether the timber is commonly stocked in the form of logs, lumber, veneer, etc., or in special sizes such as flooring strips, or is likely to be obtainable only to special order. Although the supply position is subject to change and varies in different parts of the world, it is believed this information will be useful to intending purchasers. Before making a final selection, however, it may be advisable to consult a timber merchant.

The main part of each description consists of practical information on the technical properties of the timber in simple language with the minimum of technical terms. The information is largely based on the results of investigations carried out by research laboratories and the source of the data is hereby acknowledged. A list of the principal publications consulted—and recommended to those readers who require more detailed information—is on page 171.

The terms used to classify the timbers in respect of certain technical properties are the standard terms adopted by the Forest Products Research Laboratory of Great Britain and defined in the Laboratory's Handbook of Hardwoods (1956) and Handbook of Softwoods (1960).

Seasoning and movement. In a book of this kind it is considered sufficient to state briefly the rate at which a timber dries and the degree of deterioration due to distortion, splitting, etc., to be expected. In some cases the recommended kiln-drying schedule is mentioned; particulars of these schedules are given in Forest Products Research Laboratory Leaflet No. 42. As applied to timber, the term movement means the tendency to shrink or swell in service under varying atmospheric conditions. On the basis of a standard method of measuring the dimensional changes of small timber samples over a predetermined range of atmospheric humidity, timbers are arbitrarily classified as having small, medium or large movement values (for particulars see FPRL Leaflet No. 47).

Strength and bending properties. It is not easy to generalise about the strength of a timber because this term covers a number of specific strength properties, or mechanical properties as they are sometimes called. It is often more convenient, therefore, to indicate the strength of each timber by comparing it with a well-known standard timber and by mentioning any outstanding mechanical property. Classification according to steam-bending properties is based on the minimum bending radius of sound, clear specimens one-inch thick. Timbers are classified in one of five groups ranging from Very poor to Very good (for particulars see FPRL Leaflet No. 45).

Durability and preservative treatment. The term durability is used to describe the natural resistance of a timber to fungal decay and insect attack. For convenience timbers are roughly classified in five grades intended to indicate the useful life of the timber in contact with the ground, as follows:

Perishable (5 years or less), e.g., ramin and the *sapwood* of most timbers.
Non-durable (5–10 years), e.g., jelutong, maple, silver beech, rimu.
Moderately durable (10–15 years), e.g., keruing, meranti, karri, kauri.
Durable (15–25 years), e.g., oak, deodar, totara.
Very durable (more than 25 years), e.g., teak, kapur, sal, ironbark, turpentine.

Resistance to the attack of specific insects (and also marine borers) is mentioned where appropriate.

It is sometimes more convenient to use a non-durable timber treated with a preservative than a naturally durable timber. Some timbers are readily impregnated with preservatives whereas others are more or less impermeable and cannot be given a satisfactory treatment. Where a long service life is required under conditions

favourable to decay or insect attack it is important to choose a timber that will absorb an adequate amount of preservative. The terms used to describe amenability to preservative treatment are self-explanatory. It should be noted that they refer to *heartwood*; the sapwood is usually much more permeable.

Uses. The section on uses cites some of the more typical uses of the timber in question and, where appropriate, indicates its suitability for various purposes in comparison with other species, bearing in mind that suitability may depend as much on economic factors, such as availability, price and sizes, as the technical and aesthetic properties of the timber. This section reflects the editor's personal knowledge of timber utilisation in Britain but much of the information will be found to apply in other countries as well.

Metrication

Great Britain is now committed to the adoption of the metric system in commerce and industry. It will be some time before the change is complete in all fields and during the transitional period both imperial (foot/inch) measure and metric will be in use for timber. To meet this situation numerical data are expressed in metric units as well as in the traditional form. The figures given are approximate; for greater accuracy the conventional British units of measurement used for timber may be converted to metric units by using the appropriate conversion factor as follows:

To convert inches to mm. multiply by 25·4
    ,,   ,,   feet to m. multiply by 0·305
    ,,   ,,   lb./ft.^{3} to kg./m.^{3} multiply by 16·02.

It has been agreed between the major softwood-producing countries and the principal European importing countries, including Britain, that the change to the metric system of measurement shall be based on a conventional metric inch or new inch of 25 mm. The opportunity has been taken to adopt a rationalised range of sawn softwood sizes related to those which have been in common use in the United Kingdom. They are set out in British Standard 4471 : 1969, *Specification for Dimensions for Softwood.*

Asian Timbers
HARDWOODS

Amboyna

[Pterocarpus indicus]

Distribution and supplies. Amboyna wood was originally obtained from the island of that name in the Molucca group. It is derived from *Pterocarpus indicus* and possibly other allied species in the East Indies, including the Philippines (where it is known as narra), Borneo and New Guinea. The trees vary greatly in size; they may grow to nearly 1 m. (say, 3 ft.) in diameter and are typically of poor form with wide-spreading buttresses.

General description. On the world market amboyna is best known in the form of highly figured reddish-brown veneers obtained from burrs, resembling thuya burr. Unfigured wood is golden-brown or sometimes red; the grain may be straight, interlocked or wavy, the texture rather coarse and uneven. Density is exceptionally variable, from 0·39 to 0·94 (24–59 lb./ft.³), average probably about 0·64 (40 lb./ft.³), seasoned.

Technical properties. Sawn timber is reported to dry well with little degrade and is stable in use. It should probably be classed as durable or very durable. Reports on working properties are conflicting, probably because the wood is so variable in character, but it is reputed to turn well and takes a good polish after filling. Burr wood should be cut into veneers not less than 1 mm. ($\frac{1}{25}$ in.) thick to obviate breaking.

Uses. Locally this timber is highly valued for furniture manufacture. Outside the countries of origin it is used in the form of burr veneer for high-grade cabinet work.

Other species of interest. *Maidu or mai dou of Vietnam (*P. pedatus*) also furnishes burrs which have been exported to Europe for conversion to veneer, known in Britain as false amboyna.*

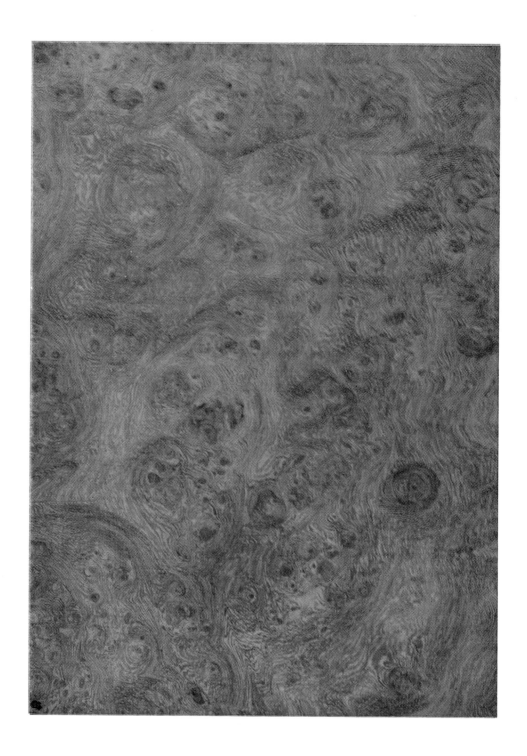

Amboyna
Burr

Reproduced two-thirds actual size

Cinnamon Wood

[various species of *Cinnamomum*]

Species of *Cinnamomum* are more familiar as products other than timber. Camphor, now made synthetically, was formerly obtained by distillation of the wood and leaves of *C. camphora*. Cinnamon comes from the bark of *C. zeylanicum*.

Distribution and supplies. Species of *Cinnamomum* are widely distributed through South-East Asia, Southern China, Formosa, Japan and southwards to Queensland, Australia; those of economic importance, such as *C. camphora* and *C. zeylanicum*, have been widely planted in tropical and sub-tropical parts of the world. Many are medium-sized trees, 18–30 m. (60–100 ft.) in height and 0·6–1·2 m. (2–4 ft.) in diameter.

The timber is nowadays available on the world market in only very small quantities, almost entirely in the form of veneer.

General description. Cinnamon wood is characterised by its scent, varying slightly from species to species, but typically pleasant and spicy. The heartwood varies in colour from pale to medium-brown, sometimes fairly plain but in some trees with darker brown or reddish stripes which, if combined with irregular grain, give a somewhat bizarre effect, as illustrated. The texture is moderately fine and the grain commonly interlocked, occasionally rather wild. The density varies according to the species; camphor wood is fairly light, 0·48–0·64 (30–40 lb./ft.^{3}), seasoned, but some other species have a rather denser wood.

Technical properties. Little is known of the technical properties of the cinnamon woods. Camphor wood, one of the lighter timbers, is reported to dry without difficulty. It has a tendency to warp but is moderately stable in use, works easily but is relatively weak and brittle, and is said to be durable, except possibly when exposed to termite attack.

Uses. Figured veneer is used for cabinet work. In the Far East the timber is used for trunks, chests and coffins.

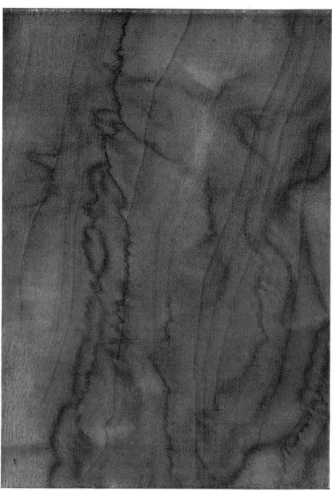

Cinnamon Wood

Butt

Reproduced actual size

Ebony, Borneo

[various species of *Diospyros*]

Diospyros is a large genus widely distributed in the tropics. The timbers vary in character: in the majority the heartwood is poorly developed and the wood has a fairly uniform, often somewhat drab, pale colour; commercially such woods are not ebonies and are of little economic interest, with the exception of persimmon (*D. virginiana*) of the South-Eastern United States. The commercial ebonies are those with a well-developed black or dark streaked heartwood. They can be divided into two groups, those such as Ceylon ebony (*D. ebenum*) and certain West African ebonies (notably *D. crassiflora*) which have a more or less uniformly black wood, and those with a striped, veined or mottled heartwood, such as Macassar ebony (*D. rumphii* and *D. celebica*), Ceylon coromandel (*D. quaesita*) and the Borneo ebony illustrated (possibly *D. durianoides*).

Distribution and supplies. In Sabah (North Borneo) alone there are five or six species—probably more—that are potential sources of ebony. Mostly they are rather small trees with boles 4·5–9·0 m. (15–30 ft.) in length and up to nearly 1 m. (say, 3 ft.) in diameter. Good quality ebony of exploitable size is rare in Sabah. It comes to the market as logs or billets free of sapwood, of a size that can be conveniently removed from the forest, often by manpower.

General description. In one species of Borneo ebony (*D. pendula*) the heartwood is black; in others it is black with streaks of reddish-brown, as illustrated. The overall effect depends on the relative proportions and distribution of the two colours in the wood and on the method of conversion. Thus quarter-cut material has a fairly regular stripe figure while on flat or rotary-cut surfaces the markings are more irregular. The wide sapwood is pale, often pinkish and uniform in colour. Borneo ebonies have a heavy heartwood, usually in the density range 0·80–0·95 (50–60 lb./ft.³), seasoned; the grain is straight or sometimes slightly wavy and may be interlocked; the texture is typically fine and fairly even.

Technical properties. Effective utilisation of heavy, decorative hardwoods like ebony depends largely on their being dried without excessive degrade and on their ease of working; other technical properties are of minor importance. Borneo ebony is difficult to season, particularly in large sizes, since it tends to develop fine, deep cracks as it dries out. Drying must be very slow and it is advisable to convert logs to the smallest convenient size as soon as possible after felling and use end-coating to minimise checking. Once dry, the ebonies have a high reputation for stability. They are brittle and extremely hard to work with both hand and machine tools and have a considerable dulling effect on cutting edges. The wood should be firmly held in the machines in order to prevent it from riding or chattering on the cutters. It turns well and can be polished to an excellent finish. It can be cut successfully for veneer. All-black ebony has a reputation for high natural resistance to fungal and termite attack.

Uses. Borneo ebony is exploited solely for its ornamental value and commands a high price; it is used for veneers, for inlays in high-class furniture and cabinet work and as solid timber for brush backs, fancy-goods and small turned articles.

16

Ebony, Borneo

Flat cut

Reproduced actual size

BO

Ebony, Ceylon

[Diospyros ebenum]

Distribution and supplies. Ceylon ebony, or East Indian ebony as it is sometimes called, is the original ebony of commerce. The tree attains its best development in Ceylon—up to 0·6 m. (2 ft.) diameter—and is also found in strictly limited quantities in southern India. Formerly, Ceylon exported large quantities of ebony all over the world but supplies have greatly diminished, as also the demand.

General description. The heartwood is black, sometimes with irregular brown streaks, extremely heavy, with a density of about 1·17 (73 lb./ft.^{3}) and an extremely fine, even texture. Grain straight or slightly irregular. The sapwood, grey with black streaks, is generally removed before logs reach the market.

Technical properties. To minimise splitting it is advisable to convert logs to small sizes and allow them to dry slowly under cover. For kiln drying FPRL schedule C is suggested. No standard strength data are available but the heartwood is known to be extremely hard and strong but brittle. It is highly resistant to insect and fungus attack. Like other varieties of ebony it is extremely hard to work and has a considerable dulling effect on cutting edges. In planing wood with irregular or curly grain, the cutting angle should be reduced to 20°. Ceylon ebony finishes to a beautifully smooth bright surface.

Uses. Ceylon ebony is traditionally used in the manufacture of musical instruments, notably for piano keys and the finger-boards of violins and 'cellos, for the handles of small tools and cutlery, brush backs, the butts of billiard cues, small articles of turnery, inlay and cabinet work. It has been largely replaced by other species of ebony or by plastics.

Other species of interest. *Coromandel or calamander wood (*Diospyros quaesita)* has grey or brown mottling. Other Indian species of ebony, notably* D. melanoxylon *and* D. tomentosa, *are used locally for carving and ornamental work. Marblewood from the Andaman Islands (*D. marmorata) *is described separately.*

18

Ebony, Ceylon
Flat cut

 Reproduced actual size

Ebony, Macassar

[*Diospyros rumphii* and *D. celebica*]

Distribution and supplies. Macassar ebony is found in the coastal forests of Celebes. The trees are of small to medium size, attaining a diameter of about 0·6 m. (2 ft.). After felling, the red-brown sapwood is removed and the striped or variegated heartwood is then cross-cut into lengths of about 3 m. (10 ft.) preparatory to seasoning and export.

General description. There is considerable variation in the colouring of the heartwood. The most characteristic type of figure is alternating light and dark stripes, as seen on quarter-cut veneer. The grain is usually fairly straight and the texture fine and uniform. The density in the seasoned condition is about 1·12 (70 lb./ft.^{3}).

Seasoning. Like most other dense, hard timbers, Macassar ebony loses its moisture slowly and any attempt to hasten drying is liable to cause splitting. This applies more particularly to the heartwood. Air seasoning under cover, with shelter from the prevailing wind and direct sunlight, is recommended.

Strength and bending properties. Macassar ebony has outstanding crushing strength along the grain, but the heartwood is brittle in comparison with the sapwood.
Except in the form of thin veneers the timber is unsuitable for steam bending. Even veneers are brittle and require careful handling when dry.

Durability. The heartwood is reputed to be very resistant to fungal attack.

Working and finishing properties. The timber is too hard to saw easily and the fine sawdust is irritant. Turning in the lathe offers little difficulty. Planing by hand is arduous and is better accomplished with a 'high-pitched' or 'Liverpool lean' plane. In machine planing, the cutting angle should be reduced to 20° and the wood must be held down firmly or it will ride on the cutters.

Uses. In the solid, Macassar ebony is used to a limited extent for ornamental purposes, such as inlaying, carving and turned goods. In veneer form it is used for cabinet work and panelling. Fancy articles, brush backs, ornamental combs and similar goods are manufactured locally in Celebes.

Ebony, Macassar

Flat cut

Reproduced actual size

Quarter cut

Rotary cut

Elm, Japanese

[various species of *Ulmus*]

Distribution and supplies. Commercial Japanese elm is derived from *Ulmus laciniata, U. davidiana* and other species, widely distributed in Japan and on the mainland of North-East Asia. The trees are of the same order of size as European elms, up to 30 m. (100 ft.) in height and 1 m. (3 ft. or more) in diameter, but being forest grown they tend to be of better form than the hedgerow elms commonly grown in Britain. The timber has been exported to Europe in small quantities as square-edged boards and strips and as veneer and has been sold in Britain under the Japanese name of nire.

General description. Japanese elm, as shipped to Europe, is typically of slow, even growth, relatively free from the defects and irregularities characteristic of English elm. It is light-brown with a fairly straight grain, open texture and generally rather plain appearance, more like American white elm than English elm. The density of the seasoned timber is of the order of 0·58 (36 lb./ft.^{3}).

Technical properties. The limited information available indicates that with reasonable care the timber can be seasoned satisfactorily. Strength is of the same order as that of selected, clear English elm. The more even growth, straighter grain and relative freedom from defects combine to make it superior to the general run of English elm in its working and finishing qualities and dimensional movement in service. There is some evidence that, like most elm, it bends well.

Uses. Japanese elm has been used in Britain for furniture, in much the same way as English elm, notably for chair seats, and for coffins. It has also been seen as the face veneer of decorative plywood. Uses in Japan include furniture, turnery and tool handles.

Elm, Japanese
Quarter cut

 Reproduced actual size

Geronggang

[Cratoxylon arborescens]

Distribution and supplies. Geronggang is locally common in Malaysia and Indonesia, though not plentiful enough to rank as an important commercial timber. It is a fairly large tree, up to nearly 1 m. (say, 3 ft.) in diameter; large logs are often hollow or affected by brittleheart. In Malaya the timber is cut to board sizes and may be sold as meranti. Consignments of lumber have been shipped to Europe, including Britain, from time to time and small parcels of logs are said to have been sent to Shanghai for veneer manufacture.

General description. A light hardwood of good, plain appearance. Heartwood brick-red, darkening on exposure, resembling dark-red meranti in colour but nearer light-red meranti and African mahogany in weight, average density about 0·55 (34 lb./ft.^{3}) in the seasoned condition. Grain straight or slightly interlocked; texture rather coarse but even. Planed surfaces are only slightly lustrous.

Technical properties. The timber is reported to dry rapidly and without difficulty. The strength is not of a high order; the results of laboratory tests on sound timber, free of brittleheart, indicate that it is inferior to light-red meranti except in its resistance to shock. It is not durable under exposed conditions but absorbs preservatives readily. It can be sawn and worked without difficulty and generally planes to a smooth surface but tools are rapidly blunted, probably because of the silica in the wood.

Uses. Geronggang is a general-utility light hardwood suitable, as an alternative to light-red meranti and similar timbers, for cheap furniture and light construction where there is no risk of fungal attack. In Malaya it has been found technically suitable for plywood but the prevalence of brittleheart and the tendency for logs to split may make this usage uneconomic.

Geronggang

Flat cut

Reproduced actual size

Haldu

[Adina cordifolia]

Distribution and supplies. Haldu (the Indian name) is widely distributed in India, Burma (where it is known as hnaw) and Thailand (kwao or kwow). It is a large tree with a straight, fluted stem; logs up to 1·25 m. (4 ft.) in diameter are not uncommon. It is an important timber in the countries of origin, being generally available and in steady demand.

General description. A general utility timber of excellent quality, usually of plain appearance though figured material is sometimes found. The thick yellowish-white sapwood merges into the yellowish-brown heartwood. The texture is fine and even, the grain fairly straight with a tendency to be spiral or interlocked near the centre of the log. Density is about 0·66 (41 lb./ft.³), seasoned, i.e., slightly lighter than beech.

Seasoning and movement. The timber seasons fairly well but has a large dimensional movement in service.

Strength properties. It is slightly inferior to teak in most respects but appreciably harder and stronger in resistance to shear stresses.

Durability and preservative treatment. A non-durable timber. There is no information on preservative treatment.

Working and finishing properties. It is easy to saw and is described as one of the nicest Indian woods to work by either hand or machine. For turnery in particular it is considered as good as beech though slightly more brittle. It takes stain evenly and polishes well.

Uses. In India haldu is utilised in much the same way as beech in Europe, though its range of uses is wider. Typical uses are turnery products (notably bobbins and tubes for the textile industry), furniture, carving, boxes and packing cases. It is also used for door and window frames and house building. Selected figured material is suitable for panelling and interior fittings. As flooring it wears evenly and is classed as suitable for ballrooms as an alternative to maple.

Haldu

Flat cut

 Reproduced actual size

'Indian Laurel'

[three species of *Terminalia*]

Formerly regarded as a single species, *Terminalia tomentosa*, the timber known as 'Indian laurel' is now considered to come from three closely allied species, *T. alata*, *T. coriacea* and *T. crenulata*. There is some evidence that figured timber is the product of the last-named species.

Distribution and supplies. The trees are widely distributed and common throughout India and Burma. The best figured timber comes from South India and Burma where the trees commonly grow to about 1 m. (say, 3 ft. or more) in diameter. Large quantities of timber are available. As a rule only specially selected material is exported; it is available as logs for conversion to veneer and as square-edged material, 25–150 mm. (1–6 in.) thick, 100–225 mm. (4–9 in.) wide and 1·8–4·2 m. (6–14 ft.) long.

General description. The heartwood coloration is irregular, light walnut-brown to dark chocolate, often banded or streaked, producing a highly decorative effect. The grain may be straight or irregular; the texture is rather coarse. Density averages about 0·85 (53 lb./ft.³), seasoned.

Seasoning and movement. It is essential to dry the timber slowly and as evenly as possible, otherwise degrade in the form of surface checking, warping and splitting may cause serious loss. Logs stored in the open are liable to develop shakes from pith to bark. The practice of felling in the wet season, followed by prompt conversion and stacking under cover or with protection from direct sunshine gives satisfactory results. Kiln seasoning can be more effective provided that temperatures and humidities are carefully controlled. FPRL kiln schedule C is recommended. There is a marked differential shrinkage during drying, tangential shrinkage being nearly 50 per cent greater than radial.

Strength properties. A very hard wood, superior to teak in most strength properties.

Durability and preservative treatment. Under tropical conditions it is moderately durable. Despite the compact nature of the wood it is amenable to preservative treatment, which is advisable when the timber is to be exposed to possible insect or fungus attack.

Working and finishing properties. The timber is difficult to work with hand tools and not very easy even with machine tools. Interlocked grain is liable to cause tearing of the surface, especially of quarter-sawn stock. A reduction of the cutting angle to not more than 20° is desirable in planing. Filling is essential if a high-gloss finish is required.

Uses. In India and Burma 'Indian laurel' is widely used in building and construction, harbour work and boat building and as railway sleepers; also for high-class furniture and panelling. After the first world war selected figured logs were introduced to the British market, mainly for interior joinery and veneered decorative panelling in public buildings and passenger liners. The timber is used occasionally for exterior solids in high-quality contract furniture.

'Indian Laurel'

Flat cut

Reproduced actual size

Rotary cut

Quarter cut

Indian Silver-Grey Wood

[Terminalia bialata]

Distribution and supplies. This species is found in the Andaman Islands where it grows to a large size with a diameter of 0·75–1·5 m. (2½–5 ft.). The trade name Indian silver-grey wood refers to the figured heartwood which is found only in certain trees, estimated as about one in five.

General description. The heartwood, when present, is greyish-brown with irregular dark markings, producing a highly ornamental figure, suggesting walnut and resembling the abnormal heartwood of the allied West African species, *Terminalia superba* (afara or limba). The plain unfigured wood, known as white chuglam, is a uniform greyish-yellow. Both types of timber are fairly straight grained, of medium texture and moderate density, average about 0·67 (42 lb./ft.³), seasoned, i.e., slightly heavier than afara.

Seasoning. The timber can be dried under cover or in a kiln with little degrade. FPRL kiln schedule E is recommended.

Strength properties. In the seasoned condition white chuglam has been found to have about the same bending strength, compressive strength along the grain, resistance to impact loads and resistance to indentation as English oak, but is about 30 per cent stiffer.

Durability and preservative treatment. This species is classed as moderately durable. Indian silver-grey wood is extremely resistant to impregnation with preservatives; white chuglam is probably moderately resistant.

Working and finishing properties. Both types of timber can be worked fairly easily with hand and machine tools and have only a slight dulling effect on cutting edges. The wood takes a smooth, silky finish from the tool.

Uses. Indian silver-grey wood has been used in Britain for ornamental panelling, cabinet work and interior fittings in public buildings and railway coaches. The non-ornamental white chuglam is used in India in building construction, oars, masts and spars and for other purposes.

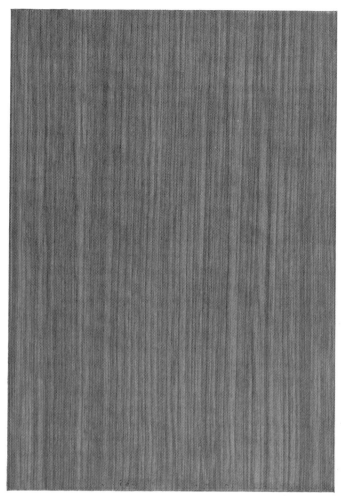

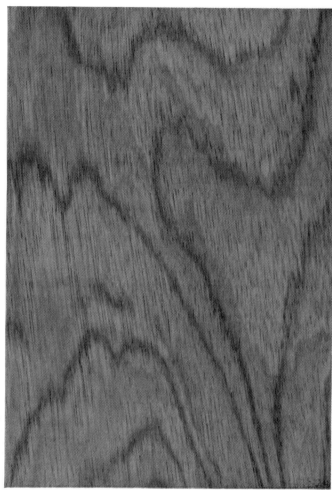

Indian Silver-Grey Wood

Quarter cut

Reproduced actual size

Flat cut

Jelutong

[Dyera costulata and *D. lowii]*

Distribution and supplies. Species of *Dyera* are large trees, up to 60 m. (200 ft.) in height and 1 m. or more (say, 3–4 ft.) in diameter, with straight, cylindrical, unbuttressed boles, often 27·5 m. (90 ft.) long. Only *D. costulata* occurs in Malaya but both species are found in Sumatra and Borneo, including Sarawak and Sabah. The two species are similar as regards their timber, which has been exported in small quantities. In Britain it is stocked in the form of lumber, 25–100 mm. (1–4 in.) thick, 100–300 mm. (4–12 in.) wide, in lengths up to 4·25 m. (14 ft.).

General description. A plain wood, uniformly white or straw-coloured throughout, although sometimes discoloured by staining fungi. The grain is straight and the texture fine and even. Jelutong is a light hardwood, average density about 0·46 (29 lb./ft.³), i.e., about the same weight as poplar. Its appearance is marred by the presence of slit-like latex traces, about 1·0 mm. (say, $\frac{1}{2}$ in.) in length (see colour plate) and tending to occur in rows at intervals of 600–900 mm. (2–3 ft.) along the grain.

Seasoning and movement. Rapid drying in the early stages is essential to prevent fungal staining. With thick stock an antiseptic chemical dip is recommended. Apart from a tendency to stain, the timber dries quickly with little degrade. FPRL kiln schedule H is recommended. Once seasoned, jelutong has only a small movement in service.

Strength properties. A light-weight wood, jelutong is correspondingly low in strength. On average it is from 25–40 per cent weaker than light-red meranti or light-red seraya in bending strength, compression, stiffness and shock resistance.

Durability and preservative treatment. Jelutong is rated non-durable when exposed to fungal attack. It is particularly susceptible to termite attack and the sapwood, although not visually distinct from the heartwood, is very liable to stain and to damage by wood-boring insects. The wood is readily treated with preservatives.

Working and finishing properties. Jelutong presents no difficulty in working with either machine or hand tools. It has little dulling effect and provided that cutting edges are kept sharp it takes an excellent finish. It nails and screws well and can be glued satisfactorily.

Uses. By reason of its fine, even texture, good working properties and stability, jelutong has been found acceptable, as an alternative to the more expensive yellow pine, for engineers' patterns and drawing boards. It is popular for model making and handicraft work and has been used for joinery.

Jelutong

Flat cut

Reproduced actual size

Kapur

[various species of *Dryobalanops*]

Kapur is the principal trade name for this timber, which has also been sold as Borneo camphorwood, Brunei teak and mahoborn teak.

Distribution and supplies. The species concerned are distributed over part of Malaya, Sumatra and Borneo, including Sabah, Sarawak and Brunei. The trees grow to a very large size, with straight boles clear of branches to a height of 30 m. (100 ft.) or more and up to nearly 3 m. (say, 10 ft.) in diameter, more usually about 1 m. (3–4 ft.). The timber is shipped to Europe and elsewhere and is available as lumber, 25–100 mm. (1–4 in.) thick, 50–300 mm. (6–12 in.) wide, in lengths up to about 7·5 m. (24 or 25 ft.). It may also be available as logs up to about 1 m. (3–4 ft.) in diameter and about 9 m. (30 ft.) long.

General description. Kapur is a high-class timber of plain appearance, reddish-brown in colour. It has a superficial resemblance to the botanically allied keruing but is, in general, more uniform in character, has a finer texture and, unlike keruing, is not gummy. A camphor-like odour is apparent when the wood is worked. In the seasoned condition the density is mostly in the range 0·72–0·80 (45–50 lb./ft.^{3}), Malayan kapur being marginally heavier than that from Sabah.

Seasoning and movement. This timber dries slowly but generally satisfactorily in thicknesses up to 25 mm., although with some tendency to cup and end-split. In thicker stock both surface- and end-splitting may be severe. FPRL kiln schedule G is recommended.

Shrinkage on drying is somewhat less than that of keruing and its stability in use rather better, with a medium movement rating.

Strength and bending properties. Kapur is roughly equal to teak in most strength properties except that, when air-dry, it is distinctly stronger in bending and compression and somewhat stronger in shear. From limited tests, it appears to be unsuitable for steam bending.

Durability and preservative treatment. The heartwood is very resistant to fungal attack but not resistant to termites. It cannot be readily treated with preservatives. The trees are sometimes attacked by a minute borer (needle worm) which makes very small holes in the wood; neither this nor the ambrosia (pin-hole) borer, which causes occasional damage in freshly felled timber, can survive in seasoned wood.

Working and finishing properties. When dry the wood presents some difficulty in working. Like keruing, it contains silica, which has a sufficiently severe blunting effect, especially on saws, to justify the use of teeth tipped with a hard metal. High-speed steel cutters give a reasonable output and satisfactory finish in planing and moulding although, as edges become dull, there is some tendency to a fibrous finish. The timber, although heavy, can be rotary-peeled. Iron staining is liable to occur under moist conditions.

Uses. Kapur is superior to keruing in respect of durability and stability; it is also more uniform in character and non-resinous. It is suitable for heavy constructional work where there is no risk of termites, and is popular locally for boat building. It is recommended for high-class joinery, both interior and exterior, such as sills, thresholds, staircases, window and door frames, cladding and garden furniture.

34

D1582422

Kapur

Flat cut

Reproduced actual size

Katsura

[Cercidiphyllum japonicum]

Distribution and supplies. Katsura is found in Japan and China as a tree up to 25 m. (say, 80 ft.) high and 1·25 m. (4 ft.) diameter. The timber is of some importance in Japan and has been exported to Britain as square-edged material up to 75 mm. (3 in.) thick, in widths of 150 mm. (6 in.) and up and lengths of 1·8 m. (6 ft.) and up.

General description. A light hardwood of plain but pleasing appearance, reddish-brown, straight grained with an exceptionally fine, even texture, of the type of American whitewood (yellow poplar) or basswood. Density variable, 0·40–0·53 or more (25–33 lb./ft.^{3} or more), average about 0·47 (29 lb./ft.^{3}), seasoned.

Technical properties. The timber can be dried without difficulty and is stable in service, comparing favourably with yellow pine in this respect. It is soft and not particularly strong, moderately durable and fairly resistant to preservative treatment. Working and finishing properties are considered to be outstandingly good. It is easy to work by hand or machine and takes an excellent smooth finish from the tool.

Uses. The combination of excellent working qualities, stability and fine, even texture makes this timber eminently suitable for mouldings, models, carving, wood engraving and handicraft work. It has been suggested for engineers' patterns as an alternative to yellow pine. In Japan it is also used for drawing boards, pencils, and as a base for lacquered cabinet work.

Katsura

Flat cut

 Reproduced actual size

Kempas

[*Koompassia malaccensis*]

Distribution and supplies. Kempas is found in Malaysia and Indonesia. In the Malay Peninsula it is reported to be common but scattered. It grows to a large size, 55 m. (180 ft.) in height and 1 m. or more (say, 4 ft.) in diameter, with a straight cylindrical bole above the buttresses, clear of branches to a height of 25 m. or so (say, 80–90 ft.). Supplies are limited by the scattered occurrence of the trees. However, the timber is in regular use in Malaya and has been exported to Britain in small quantities.

General description. A hard, heavy wood of distinctive appearance, brick red, darkening to orange-red with yellow-brown streaks which make it appear rather coarse textured. Grain typically interlocked. A characteristic feature is the presence of veins of hard, stony tissue. The average density is about 0·87 (54 lb./ft.^{3}), seasoned.

Seasoning. The timber normally seasons fairly well. Splits are liable to develop in association with the veins of abnormal tissue. FPRL kiln schedule E is suggested.

Strength properties. On the basis of laboratory tests kempas is classed as a heavy constructional timber, similar to Australian karri in most strength properties.

Durability and preservative treatment. Limited tests indicate that kempas is similar to oak in its resistance to fungal attack. Under tropical conditions it is liable to be attacked by termites but preservative treatment gives effective protection.

Working and finishing properties. The timber is hard to work with hand tools and hand sawing is not economic, but sawmill conversion is satisfactory provided suitable saws and correct rates of feed are adopted. Working and finishing properties generally are somewhat similar to those of a dense grade of keruing.

Uses. As a constructional timber, comparable to keruing but appreciably heavier, kempas appears to be more suitable for local use than for export. It has been found satisfactory in Malaya for the manufacture of veneer for plywood core. It might well prove acceptable for high-class hardwood flooring.

Other species of interest. *A closely allied species in Sabah is known as impas. The timber resembles kempas except that it is some 30 per cent heavier. Supplies are limited and the timber is not likely to be available for export in quantity.*

Kempas

Flat cut

Reproduced actual size

Keruing and allied timbers

[various species of *Dipterocarpus*]

Distribution and supplies. Timber of the keruing type, produced by more than seventy species of *Dipterocarpus*, occurs in parts of India and Pakistan, Ceylon, throughout South-East peninsular Asia, and in Sumatra, Borneo and the Philippines. The timber is known by distinctive names according to its origin; among the more important are keruing (Malaya, Sarawak, Sabah and Indonesia), gurjun (India and Burma), yang (Thailand), apitong (Philippines). The general characters of the timbers from the different countries are similar, but where the timber is produced by comparatively few species, as in Burma and Thailand, shipments tend to be more uniform in character than those from countries, such as Malaya and Sabah, with a large number of species. The trees commonly reach a large size, 30–60 m. (100–200 ft.) in height, with a straight, cylindrical bole 0·9–1·8 m. (3–6 ft.) in diameter. The timber is in good supply. In Britain it is available in the form of graded lumber, 25–150 mm. (1–6 in.) thick, 100–350 mm. (4–14 in.) wide, in lengths of 1·8–6·0 m. (6–20 ft.) or more, average about 4·25 m. (14 ft.), and as flooring strips. Logs are 300–750 mm. (12–30 in.) in diameter and 3·5–12·0 m. (12–40 ft.) long.

General description. A timber of plain appearance, varying in colour and density according to species. The heartwood is pinkish-brown to dark-brown, sometimes with a purple tint, usually distinct from the pale sapwood. In the seasoned condition the density is mostly in the range 0·72–0·80 (45–50 lb./ft.^{3}), i.e., comparable to English oak or a little heavier. The grain is straight or slightly interlocked; the texture typically rather coarse. The timber is remarkably free from defects, though resin exudation is liable to mar the surface of the wood, particularly when it is exposed to direct sunlight or radiant heat.

Seasoning and movement. Keruing and allied timbers dry rather slowly. There is a tendency for distortion and collapse to occur. To reduce the risk of resin exudation in service the timber may be raised to a high temperature in the kiln to drive off the volatile component. Any resin that comes to the surface during seasoning can be cleaned off before the timber is used. FPRL kiln schedule D is recommended. Dimensional movement in service is classed as large.

Strength and bending properties. On average, the timbers of this group are some 40 per cent stiffer than oak and 20 per cent superior in bending and compression. They are considered unsuitable for steam-bending work.

Durability and preservative treatment. The heartwood is moderately durable against fungal attack but is susceptible to termites. It is rated moderately resistant to preservative treatment.

Working and finishing properties. In the green condition the timber can be sawn and machined without serious difficulty, but once dried it often gives trouble, owing to the silica content, and the use of tungsten carbide tipped tools, especially saws, is advisable. It can be machined to a clean, if slightly fibrous, surface; where the grain is interlocked, the finish of quartered surfaces is improved by reducing the cutting angle to 20°. Resin adhering to tools, fences and machine tables is sometimes troublesome and has an adverse effect on finishing treatments.

Uses. Because of its comparatively low cost and good technical properties keruing is largely used in place of oak for constructional work in ships, boats and road vehicles, for flooring, for decking on piers and wharves and for exterior cladding. It is used for plywood manufacture in Asia.

Keruing
Quarter cut

 Reproduced actual size

Kokko

[Albizia lebbek]

Distribution and supplies. Kokko has a wide distribution in India, Ceylon, Burma and the Andaman Islands, extending as far as Northern Malaya. It is extensively cultivated, especially as a roadside tree. At its best it is a fine large tree, up to nearly 1 m. (say, 3 ft.) in diameter, yielding squares 3–9 m. (10–30 ft.) in length and 300–750 mm. (12–30 in.) side measurement. The largest supplies are available from the Andamans.

General description. A handsome dark-brown wood with lighter streaks. At one time it was sold as East Indian walnut but it is coarser in texture than walnut, with irregular interlocked grain, more like iroko in general appearance. Average density is about 0·64 (40 lb./ft.^{3}), seasoned.

Seasoning. A moderately refractory timber; logs are liable to severe end-splitting and should be end-coated; end-splitting and surface cracking may also occur during air drying of lumber but with care boards up to 25 mm. (1 in.) thick can be seasoned satisfactorily; in thicker material the rate of drying is very slow. Kiln seasoning is said to present no difficulty and degrade is negligible.

Strength and bending properties. In large dimensions kokko is generally similar to English oak, except in resistance to impact loads. It is not to be relied on in small sections, however, because of the irregular grain. Though rather hard to bend it has been found suitable in India for bentwood handles.

Durability and preservative treatment. In India it is classed as moderately durable. Under temperate conditions it may be expected to merit a higher rating. No information is available on preservative treatment but it may be expected to be resistant.

Working and finishing properties. Kokko presents some difficulty in working, partly on account of its density and also because of the irregular grain. For planing, particularly of quarter-sawn material, a cutting angle of not more than 20° should be used. The fine dust produced in sawing and sanding is irritating to the eyes, nose and throat. Because of its coarse texture the wood requires careful filling but can be finished to a fine glossy surface. It can be peeled or sliced to produce decorative veneer.

Uses. In India kokko is rated a timber of the first class, both for construction and for furniture, panelling and interior woodwork, as in railway passenger coaches. It is also used for wheelwrights' work. Elsewhere it is sometimes used as a decorative veneer, the dark-brown colour producing a handsome if rather sombre effect.

Kokko

Quarter cut

Reproduced actual size

Lauan

[species of *Shorea, Parashorea* and *Pentacme*]

Lightweight timbers of *Shorea, Parashorea* and *Pentacme* are known in the Philippines by the name lauan, which is broadly equivalent to Malayan meranti and Borneo seraya. The timbers are divided into two commercial groups: (*a*) red lauan, sometimes called Philippine red mahogany, comprising the darker-coloured timbers, and (*b*) white lauan, sometimes called Philippine light-red or white mahogany, those that are white or pale in colour.

Distribution and supplies. The lauan group of timbers is the most important contribution of the Philippines to world timber supplies. The various species concerned are large, well-formed trees, commonly reaching a height of 45 m. (say, 150 ft.) with a clear cylindrical bole of up to 28 m. (90 ft.) often occurring in pure stands. The timber is exported in large quantities, as logs, graded lumber, veneer and plywood.

General description. The timbers of this group range from nearly white to dark-red, according to species and locality of growth. The average density varies between about 0.50 and 0.66 ($31–41$ lb./ft.^{3}) in the seasoned condition—about the same as the range encountered in African timbers of the mahogany family. In colour, grain, texture and technical properties they may be compared to the allied timbers Malayan meranti and Borneo seraya. They exhibit a similar range of variation but in so far as commercial consignments of lauan often consist largely of a single species, these tend to be more uniform in character. Interlocked grain, producing a broad, striped, mahogany-type figure on quartered surfaces, is characteristic of the group as a whole.

Technical properties. In general the timbers present no special difficulty in seasoning, working and finishing. They have the reputation of being dimensionally stable in service and non-durable to moderately durable. Some species are susceptible to pinhole borer damage and brittleheart is liable to occur. Strength properties vary according to species, as indicated by the density range.

Uses. Lauan is largely used for the manufacture of plywood. Lumber is used in furniture production, interior joinery and light structural work, in much the same way as African mahogany.

Lauan, Red
Flat cut

Reproduced actual size

Maple, Japanese

[various species of *Acer*]

Distribution and supplies. Maples occur in the temperate forests of Japan in great variety. They are relatively small trees, rarely more than 15 m. (50 ft.) high and 0·6 m. (2 ft.) in diameter. The timber has been exported to Britain as square-edged material, 25–50 mm. (1–2 in.) thick, 150 mm. (6 in.) and up wide, in lengths of 1·8 m. (6 ft.) and up and as flooring strips.

General description. The wood of the Japanese maples shows a wide range of variation according to species. The material exported to Britain resembles North American hard maple but the heartwood is generally a darker shade of pinkish-brown and is lighter in weight, average density about 0·66 (41 lb./ft.³), seasoned. The texture is fine and even, the grain straight or slightly irregular.

Seasoning and movement. The timber can be expected to dry without serious degrade. FPRL kiln schedule E is probably suitable but schedule A may be preferred if darkening is to be avoided. Movement in service is probably about average.

Strength and bending properties. Timber of the quality exported to Britain in the past can be assumed to be intermediate between sycamore and North American hard maple in strength and is probably suitable for steam bending if carefully selected.

Durability and preservative treatment. It is almost certainly not resistant to fungus and insect attack. The wide sapwood is permeable; the heartwood may be resistant to impregnation.

Working and finishing properties. Limited experience with Japanese maple indicates that it is appreciably harder to work than sycamore, being more like American hard maple in this respect. It generally takes a clean, smooth finish from the tool though irregular grain may cause trouble. In machine planing the cutting angle should be reduced to 20°.

Uses. Japanese maple has been used in Britain for the same purposes as hard maple, notably for flooring. Uses in Japan include turnery, tool handles and cabinet work.

Maple, Japanese

Flat cut

 Reproduced actual size

Marblewood

[Diospyros marmorata]

Distribution and supplies. Andaman marblewood or zebrawood is found throughout the Andaman Islands as a moderate-sized tree up to 0·6 m. (2 ft.) in diameter. Logs for export are reported to average 2·5–3·0 m. (8–10 ft.) in length and 200–300 mm. (8–12 in.) in diameter, the figured heartwood being rarely more than 150 mm. (6 in.) in diameter. The supply is limited.

General description. As the name implies, this is one of those ebonies with a streaked or mottled heartwood, of the type of Macassar ebony and coromandel. The greyish-brown heartwood is marked with dark-brown or black, the figure varying from a fairly regular stripe to a highly irregular pattern, depending partly on the method of conversion. It is fairly straight grained, with a fine, even texture. The average density in the seasoned condition is about 1·02 (64 lb./ft.^{3}).

Technical properties. The timber is not easy to season as it is liable to warp and develop fine end splits and surface cracks. It is difficult to saw and to plane but works, with care, to a smooth surface. It is an excellent wood for turnery, less liable to chip than black ebony. It takes a beautiful polish.

Uses. Andaman marblewood is used exclusively for ornamental work, whether in the solid form or as veneer. Typical uses are cabinet work, panelling, fancy turnery and brush backs.

Marblewood

Flat cut

Reproduced actual size

Mengkulang

[various species of *Heritiera,* formerly *Tarrietia*]

Distribution and supplies. Some half-dozen species of *Heritiera* in South-East Asia produce timber of the type known as mengkulang in Malaya, kembang in Sabah, chumprak in Thailand and lumbayao in the Philippines. In Malaya and Sabah the most frequent species is believed to be *H. simplicifolia*, a medium-sized to large tree, 30–45 m. (100–150 ft.) in height with a well-shaped bole 0·6–0·9 m. (2–3 ft.) in diameter above the buttresses. The timber is available for export in small quantities in the form of lumber and plywood.

General description. A medium-weight mahogany-like wood, resembling the closely allied West African niangon. Heartwood medium-pink to reddish-brown, shading into the paler sapwood. Grain typically interlocked and sometimes irregular. Quarter-cut material shows a broad stripe figure and, unlike mahogany, a fairly conspicuous fleck due to the large rays. The appearance of the wood is sometimes enhanced by a natural lustre. Density is mostly in the range 0·64–0·72 (40–45 lb./ft.^{3}), seasoned.

Seasoning and movement. Provided it is properly stacked the timber dries fairly rapidly and well apart from a tendency to surface checks. FPRL kiln schedule K is recommended. Once dry it is rated as having a small movement in service.

Strength properties. Mengkulang has good strength properties, being similar to teak and utile and generally superior to niangon.

Durability and preservative treatment. In Malaya mengkulang is rapidly destroyed in contact with the ground, being susceptible to attack by termites and wood-destroying fungi. It is, however, quite satisfactory for use in reasonably dry situations secure from termite attack. It is moderately resistant to preservative treatment.

Working and finishing properties. The silica in the wood has a dulling effect on tools, especially when it is sawn or worked in the seasoned condition. Saw teeth should be tipped with tungsten carbide. In planing, a standard 30° cutter block gives a satisfactory finish on flat-sawn material but for quarter-sawn surfaces a cutting angle of 20° is recommended and this produces a good smooth finish on all faces. In boring, recessing and mortising, fairly rapid blunting occurs and the finish tends to be splintery or fibrous. Mengkulang peels well and has good gluing properties. It takes an excellent polish.

Uses. In Malaya mengkulang is classed as a very good general-utility timber, suitable for interior construction, flooring, furniture and boat building. On the export market it is recommended for joinery, flooring and other purposes as an alternative to a dense type of mahogany. It makes attractive veneer and plywood.

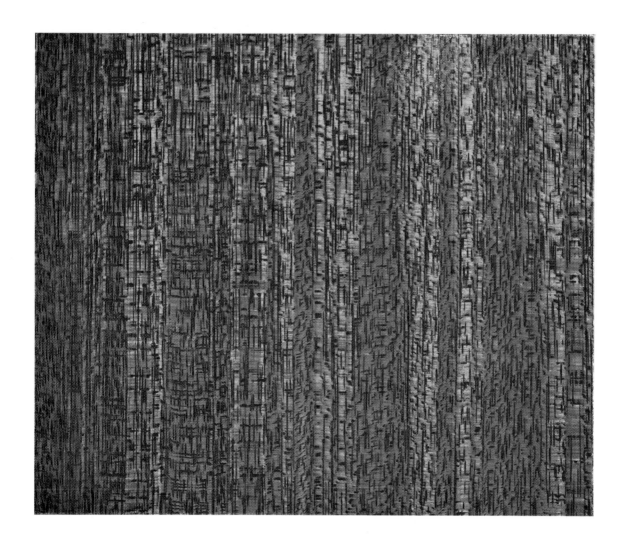

Mengkulang
Quarter cut

Reproduced actual size

Meranti or Seraya, Dark-Red

[various species of *Shorea*]

The light- to medium-weight red timbers produced by species of *Shorea* are known as red meranti in Malaya and Sarawak and red seraya in Sabah. They are sometimes marketed under these names without further distinction but for the export market the darker, usually heavier timbers are commonly separated from the others and designated dark-red meranti or dark-red seraya. The principal species in this group is *S. pauciflora*, sometimes known as nemesu in Malaya and as oba suluk in Sabah.

Distribution and supplies: The distribution of this group covers Malaya, Sumatra, the island of Borneo and the Philippine Islands. The trees reach a large size, up to 60 m. (say, 200 ft.) or more in height and 1·5 m. (5 ft.) in diameter, with a cylindrical bole above high buttresses. The timber is in good supply, though the out-turn is small compared with light-red meranti/seraya. Square-edged graded material is available in the same dimensions as light-red meranti.

General description. The timber is typically darker, harder and appreciably heavier than the better-known light-red meranti/seraya and tends to be more uniform in character. It is commonly marked with conspicuous white streaks of hardened resin. It is comparatively free from defects, being less liable to brittleheart and shot-hole borer damage than the lighter-coloured timbers. The density of seasoned timber is mostly in the range 0·58–0·77 (36–48 lb./ft.^{3}), average about 0·67 (42 lb./ft.^{3}), which is about the same as West African utile. The grain is interlocked, giving a broad stripe figure on quartered surfaces.

Seasoning and movement. The timber dries more slowly than light-red meranti, especially in thicker sizes. There is some tendency to distort and in thicker sizes there is some risk of splitting and checking. Movement in service is rated as small.

Strength and bending properties. Dark-red meranti and seraya compare favourably with utile in stiffness, toughness and shock resistance and, when comparable in weight, in bending and compression strength, but are appreciably weaker in hardness, shear and cleavage. They are of doubtful value for steam bending.

Durability and preservative treatment. Heartwood is rated moderately durable to durable, the denser grades having a greater resistance to decay. It is extremely resistant to preservative treatment.

Working and finishing properties. Although heavier, dark-red meranti and seraya, like the light-red timbers, present little difficulty in sawing and machining provided that cutters are kept reasonably sharp. The timber takes nails well. Logs can be rotary-peeled to give an attractive veneer.

Uses. Being more stable, stronger and more durable than light-red meranti/seraya, and more uniform in character, this timber is suitable for more exacting purposes, in construction, exterior joinery, for flooring under moderate conditions of wear, for ship and boat building and for framing for road vehicles.

Other species of interest. *Philippine red lauan (see p. 44) is broadly the equivalent of dark-red meranti/seraya.*

Meranti or Seraya, Dark-Red

Quarter cut

  Reproduced actual size

Meranti or Seraya, Light-Red

[various species of *Shorea*]

Light- to medium-weight timbers of species of *Shorea* are known by distinctive names according to their country of origin. Thus, meranti in Malaya and Sarawak is broadly equivalent to seraya from Sabah and lauan from the Philippines. The timbers are also distinguished according to colour, as light-red, dark-red, yellow and white.

Distribution and supplies. The distribution of this important group covers Malaya, Sumatra, the island of Borneo and the Philippines. The trees reach a large size, with well-shaped boles up to about 28–30 m. (90–100 ft.) in length and 1 m. or more (say, 3–4 ft.) in diameter. The timber is shipped in large quantities to other parts of Asia and to Europe, Australia, South Africa and elsewhere. Meranti is the principal timber exported from Malaya (mainly lumber) and seraya from Sabah (mainly logs). In Britain red meranti is commonly available as square-edged graded material, 12–100 mm. ($\frac{1}{2}$–4 in.) thick, 100–300 mm. (4–12 in.) wide, in lengths of 1·8–6·0 m. (6–20 ft.), average 3·5 m. (12 ft.), and as strips, 25 ×75 or 100 mm. (1 ×3 or 4 in.). Red seraya is more familiar in the form of plywood.

General description. Being a mixture of species, the commercial timber is unusually variable in character. The colour ranges from very pale pink to a medium-red shade. Density varies from about 0·40–0·64 (25–40 lb./ft.³), average about 0·51 (32 lb./ft.³) when dry, which is slightly below the average for African mahogany. Like mahogany, it commonly has a conspicuous broad stripe figure on quartered surfaces but is somewhat coarser textured. Brittleheart is commonly present.

Seasoning and movement. The timber seasons well apart from a marked tendency to cup; the rate of drying is fairly rapid with thin stock, but rather slow with 50 mm. (2 in.) and thicker material. FPRL kiln schedule F is suitable. Once dry, it is rated as having a small movement in service.

Strength and bending properties. The timbers of this group tend to vary in strength, but are roughly comparable to African mahogany in bending and compression, stiffness, toughness, resistance to shock and cleavage; they are markedly inferior only in hardness and shear. They are unsuitable for solid bending purposes.

Durability and preservative treatment. The timber is rated as moderately durable; the heartwood is resistant to preservative treatment and the sapwood moderately resistant. In the green condition the timber is sometimes damaged by pinhole borers and, when dry, the sapwood is susceptible to powder-post beetle attack.

Working and finishing properties. Lightweight, non-siliceous and non-gummy timbers, they present little difficulty in sawing and machining. Blunting is only slight but cutters should be kept sharp to produce a satisfactory finish, especially with lightweight timber and when surfacing quartered stock if tearing is to be avoided. The timber takes nails and screws well and can be glued satisfactorily.

Uses. A popular hardwood for inexpensive joinery, light structural work and other purposes where variation in colour, grain and texture is permissible. It has been used in prefabricated building construction and for exterior cladding and interior parts of furniture. It is an important plywood timber.

Meranti or Seraya, Light-Red

Quarter cut

Reproduced actual size

Meranti or Seraya, Yellow

[various species of *Shorea*]

Light- to medium-weight *Shorea* timbers with predominantly yellow or yellow-brown heartwood are known as yellow meranti in Malaya and Sarawak and as yellow seraya in Sabah. The only species of this group in the Philippines, known locally as kalunti, is classed as yellow lauan for trade purposes.

Distribution and supplies. The distribution of this group extends from the southern tip of Thailand, through Malaya, Sumatra and the island of Borneo to Mindanao in the Philippines. The trees are mostly medium-sized to large, with long cylindrical boles, sometimes 0·9–1·5 m. (3–5 ft.) in diameter above the buttresses. The timber is converted to the same specifications as light-red meranti/seraya, though the quantities available for export are smaller.

General description. Being a mixture of species, the commercial timber is variable in colour, weight and texture. Heartwood is typically a dull-yellow or yellow-brown, darkening somewhat on prolonged exposure; it is liable to discoloration in contact with iron under moist conditions. The grain is shallowly interlocked and the texture moderately coarse, although somewhat finer than that of red meranti. Density when dry is mostly in the range 0·56–0·67 (35–42 lb./ft.³), i.e., intermediate between that of light-red and dark-red meranti. Brittleheart is sometimes present and the appearance of the wood may be marred by the presence of pinhole borer damage.

Seasoning and movement. In thicknesses up to 50 mm. (2 in.) the timber dries slowly but well, apart from some tendency to cup; in thicker sizes moisture movement is slow and there is some risk of honeycombing. FPRL kiln schedule J is recommended. Dimensional movement in service is rated as medium.

Strength properties. Like other types of meranti the timber is somewhat variable in strength. On average, it is of the order of 10–15 per cent superior to light-red meranti/seraya in stiffness and resistance to bending, and about 25 per cent tougher, harder and more resistant to shear and splitting.

Durability and preservative treatment. Heartwood is rated moderately durable with regard to decay, but is not resistant to termite attack. Logs are susceptible to ambrosia (pinhole borer) beetle damage and, on drying, sapwood is liable to attack by powder-post beetles. Heartwood is extremely resistant to preservative treatment even under pressure.

Working and finishing properties. The timber works easily with all hand and machine tools and has only a slight blunting effect. A good finish is obtained provided sharp tools are used, although to avoid tearing when planing quartered surfaces, a cutting angle of 20° is recommended. For rip sawing, satisfactory results are obtained with saws having 54 teeth and a 25° hook.

Uses. Though slightly harder and heavier than light-red meranti, yellow meranti can be used for similar purposes, namely joinery, light structural work where some variation in colour, grain and texture is permissible, and for plywood.

Other species of interest. *White meranti is the trade name for a distinct group of* Shorea *species with nearly white heartwood, darkening to a buff colour, widely distributed in South-East Asia. The wood has a high silica content which makes it difficult to saw but it can be peeled for the manufacture of plywood. White meranti should not be confused with white seraya.*

Meranti or Seraya, Yellow

Quarter cut

 Reproduced actual size

Merbau

[Intsia bijuga and *I. palembanica]*

Distribution and supplies. Species of *Intsia* have a wide distribution, particularly *I. bijuga*, which occurs on the mainland of Asia in Vietnam, Thailand and Malaya, and from Madagascar and the Seychelles in the western Indian Ocean through the East Indies to Fiji and New Caledonia in the Western Pacific. *I. palembanica* occurs in Malaya, Sumatra and Borneo; it is a large tree and although of somewhat variable stem form, is the principal species producing the timber known as merbau in Malaya, Sarawak and Sabah, which has been exported to Britain in small quantities.

General description. *Intsia* is closely related botanically to *Afzelia* and their timbers are very similar in general character. Merbau is a coarse-textured, heavy, red-brown wood, a little darker than the general run of afzelia, especially the wood of *I. bijuga*, which is slightly darker and heavier than that of *I. palembanica*. The average density is about 0·8 (50 lb./ft.³) in the seasoned condition. The grain is usually interlocked, giving a broad stripe figure on quartered surfaces but, as with afzelia, even plain, unfigured wood has a handsome, dignified appearance.

Seasoning and movement. According to Malayan and other reports, merbau dries slowly with little degrade; its shrinkage is small and once dry it has a reputation for stability in service.

Strength properties. In its strength characteristics merbau compares closely with afzelia in bending and impact but is somewhat inferior in compression and hardness; although strong in impact it is of uncertain resilience and tends to break with a short fracture.

Durability and preservative treatment. Merbau has a reputation for high natural durability, including resistance to termite attack. It is not the sort of timber that requires preservative treatment.

Working and finishing properties. Merbau is rather difficult to work; saw teeth, although not badly blunted, tend to become covered with gum. It cuts cleanly in most operations, but quarter-sawn stock tends to tear a little in planing unless a cutting angle of about 20° is used. The timber usually splits when nailed; it takes stains and polishes satisfactorily and has an attractive natural finish.

Uses. A high-class, stable, durable, rather heavy hardwood with an attractive appearance. It is suitable for the same purposes as afzelia, such as high-class joinery for interior and exterior work and for flooring, except for heavy-duty traffic. Like afzelia, it contains a yellow dyestuff and should not be used for purposes such as draining boards where it is liable to come into contact with wet fabrics.

58

Merbau

Quarter cut

Reproduced actual size

Mersawa

[various species of *Anisoptera*]

Mersawa is the trade name used in Malaya and Indonesia for timber of the local species of *Anisoptera*. Timber of the same or closely allied species in neighbouring territories is known as krabak (Thailand), kaunghmu (Burma) and palosapis (Philippines).

Distribution and supplies. The geographical range of this group extends from East Pakistan and Northern Burma to the Philippines and New Guinea. All the species concerned are medium-sized to large trees, usually with straight, cylindrical boles up to 0·9–1·5 m. (3–5 ft.) in diameter, clear of branches to a height of 25–30 m. (80–100 ft.). Timber from Malaya, Burma, and Thailand has been exported to Europe since the second world war.

General description. Mersawa is a utility hardwood of plain appearance, light yellowish-brown in colour with a rather coarse texture and straight or slightly interlocked grain. The sapwood is liable to be discoloured by staining fungi. The average density varies from about 0·56 to 0·72 (35–45 lb./ft.³) in the seasoned condition.

Seasoning and movement. The timber dries very slowly, though without serious degrade. FPRL kiln schedule E has given satisfactory results. Dimensional movement of seasoned timber in service is classed as medium.

Strength and bending properties. Strength properties vary with density; most species compare favourably with timber of the light meranti type. The wood is of no value for bending work.

Durability and preservative treatment. It is classed as moderately resistant to decay; it does not absorb preservative readily even under pressure.

Working and finishing properties. All the timbers of this group contain silica in varying amounts, which has a severe blunting effect on ordinary saws and machine tools. The finished surface tends to be fibrous.

Uses. Mersawa and allied timbers were used in considerable quantities in Britain during the post-war years for general utility purposes, including flooring. Selected straight-grained logs have been found suitable for the manufacture of plywood for tea chests.

Mersawa

Quarter cut

Reproduced actual size

Nyatoh

[principally *Palaquium* spp. and *Payena* spp.]

Nyatoh is the name used in the Malayan region for medium-weight timber (density up to 0·88, i.e., 55 lb./ft.³, in the seasoned condition) of a number of closely allied species of the botanical family Sapotaceae, principally *Palaquium* spp. and *Payena* spp. Heavier timber of this group is known as bitis in Malaya and as nyatoh batu in Sabah and Sarawak.

Distribution and supplies. Species producing timber of the nyatoh type are widely distributed from India through South-East Asia to the Philippines, New Guinea and the Western Pacific Islands. The trees often reach a large size, 30 m. (100 ft.) or more in height and up to 1 m. (say, 3 ft. or more) in diameter. The timber has been exported in small quantities from Malaya. In Britain it is on offer as square-edged material up to 75 mm. (3 in.) thick, 300 mm. (12 in.) wide and 4·25 m. (14 ft.) long.

General description. Being a mixture of species, the timber is variable in colour, weight and texture. The heartwood is pale-pink to red-brown but typically a medium pinkish-brown; it sometimes resembles West African makoré, particularly in colour, grain and figure, but is more variable in character. The density is usually between 0·64 and 0·72 (40–45 lb./ft.³) but may vary from 0·53 to 0·88 (33–35 lb./ft.³), seasoned. The texture is moderately fine and the grain straight, shallowly interlocked or sometimes slightly wavy; like makoré it sometimes shows an attractive moiré or watered silk figure.

Seasoning. Experience in Asia suggests that nyatoh requires some care in drying. It air seasons rather more slowly than red meranti, with some tendency to end-split and distort.

Strength properties. Limited data on timber of about average weight suggest that nyatoh is the equal of oak in hardness and resistance to shear, is some 10–15 per cent stronger in compression and bending strength but is not as resistant to shock.

Durability and preservative treatment. The natural durability of nyatoh under temperate conditions is not known. In South-East Asia it is rated non-durable, with a low resistance to termite attack. Dry sapwood is sometimes susceptible to powder-post beetle attack. Limited tests suggest that the heartwood is very resistant to treatment by pressure impregnation methods.

Working and finishing properties. It is in its working properties that the variable character of nyatoh shows most clearly, since some species are siliceous and others are not. Non-siliceous wood saws easily, apart from a slight tendency to a build-up of gum on saws, and can be planed to a smooth surface with little picking up. In contrast, siliceous wood can be extremely abrasive and difficult to saw with standard mill equipment.

Indian experience suggests that the timber peels easily and well to make a good plywood.

Uses. The successful marketing of nyatoh for lumber probably depends on eliminating the siliceous species and selecting the timber for colour and density. Because of its uncertain durability it cannot be recommended for use in conditions favouring decay, but its good appearance and fine, even texture suggest it for inexpensive interior joinery and fittings and for furniture work.

It is a potential plywood timber and for this purpose siliceous species might well be acceptable; occasional logs contain figured wood suitable for conversion into decorative veneer.

Nyatoh

Flat cut

Reproduced actual size

Oak, Japanese

[principally *Quercus mongolica* var. *grosseserrata*]

Distribution and supplies. Japanese oak is regularly exported to Europe and other parts of the world. In Britain it is commonly available in the form of graded square-edged, plain or figured material, 12–100 mm. ($\frac{1}{2}$–4 in.) thick and 75–300 mm. (3–12 in.) wide, in lengths up to 3·5 m. (12 ft.), also as strips, 19–25 mm. ($\frac{3}{4}$–1 in.) thick by 50–125 mm. (2–5 in.) wide, and as veneer and the facings of plywood.

General description. The comparatively open texture and uniform character of Japanese oak, due to the slow, even growth (narrow rings) is often distinctive. The wood tends to be lighter in colour than European and American white oak, also lighter in weight and softer. Average density is about 0·66 (41 lb./ft.^{3}), seasoned. The grain is usually straight. The characteristic oak figure due to the broad rays is shown to advantage on quarter-cut material. In common with other species of oak, Japanese oak corrodes metals, particularly iron, steel and lead; blue-black discolorations from the tannic acid in the wood are liable to develop in contact with iron under damp conditions. For this reason the use of non-ferrous metals for fastenings and fittings is recommended; alternatively iron or steel metalwork should be galvanised or well painted.

Seasoning and movement. The timber is partly seasoned when it reaches the market. Drying may be completed with less degrade than occurs with English oak, though the process should not be hurried. Dimensional movement in service is classed as medium.

Strength and bending properties. Japanese oak is slightly inferior to other commercial varieties of oak in all strength properties and is not usually specified for purposes where strength is of prime importance. It is classed as very good for steam bending.

Durability and preservative treatment. Because it is normally used for interior work Japanese oak has not been subjected to standard tests of durability under European conditions. It can be assumed to be not greatly inferior to European oak in this respect and is almost certainly resistant to preservative treatment.

Working and finishing properties. Japanese oak is generally milder and easier to finish than other commercial varieties of oak.

Uses. Because of its easier working properties Japanese oak is often preferred to English or other European oak for furniture and interior joinery where the cost of production is a major consideration. It is not generally specified for the best class of work.

Other species of interest. *Oak from Iran (Q. castaneaefolia), known to the trade as Persian oak, is exported to Britain and elsewhere in the form of staves for the manufacture of casks.*

64

Oak, Japanese
Quarter cut

Reproduced actual size

Padauk, Andaman

[Pterocarpus dalbergioides]

Distribution and supplies. Andaman padauk is the most important timber of the Andaman Islands. A very large, buttressed tree with a straight cylindrical bole, 12 m. (40 ft.) or more to the first branch. Squared logs measure 6–7·5 m. (20–25 ft.) in length, 750 mm. (30 in.) or more side measurement. In Britain the timber may be found as square-edged material, 25–75 mm. (1–3 in.) thick, 150–350 mm. (6–14 in.) wide, up to about 5 m. (16 ft.) long, and as decorative veneer.

General description. A high-quality timber of handsome appearance, one of the most decorative Indian timbers, typically a rich crimson shade darkening to a deep purplish-brown. (Wood from certain trees is pale-red or yellowish, known as 'off-colour' padauk.) The decorative character is enhanced by the interlocked grain. The texture is rather coarse. Density is variable, average about 0·78 (49 lb./ft.^{3}), seasoned.

Seasoning and movement. The timber dries well in the air or in a kiln, without warping or splitting. It is liable to develop fine, wavy surface checks which are not very noticeable. FPRL kiln schedule F is suggested. Padauk has the reputation of being dimensionally stable in service.

Strength properties. In the seasoned condition Andaman padauk is as strong as teak and about 40 per cent harder.

Durability and preservative treatment. It is classed as very durable, being highly resistant to fungi and insects, including termites, but is liable to attack by *Teredo.* It is moderately resistant to impregnation but is not the kind of timber that requires preservative treatment.

Working and finishing properties. The timber is fairly hard to work. The interlocked grain makes it difficult to plane and a cutting angle of 15° is needed for a good finish. In most other operations it works cleanly and turns well. It responds well to finishing treatments and polishes well provided the grain is properly filled.

Uses. Andaman padauk is used for high-class interior joinery such as bank counters, panelling and balustrades and for interior fittings in ships and railway coaches. It has been used for billiard tables and is eminently suitable for decorative flooring. In India it is also used for vehicle body building and furniture.

Other species of interest. P. marsupium *is a valuable constructional timber in South India.* P. santalinus, *formerly exported from India to Europe as a dye wood, is in demand locally for decorative work in house building.* P. macrocarpus *(Burma padauk) and* P. indicus *(amboyna) are described separately.*

EI

Padauk, Andaman

Flat cut

 Reproduced two-thirds actual size

Padauk, Burma

[Pterocarpus macrocarpus]

Distribution and supplies. Burma padauk is an important timber in Burma and also in Thailand where it is known as pradoo or mai pradoo. A large tree with a straight cylindrical bole yielding squared logs commonly 7·5 m. (25 ft.) in length and 500 mm. (20 in.) side measurement. Large quantities of timber are produced, mainly for local use. It is not well known in Britain but may be obtainable on inquiry as solid timber and as veneer.

General description. The timber is distinguished from Andaman padauk in being generally harder and heavier (density about 0·85 (53 lb./ft.^{3}), seasoned) and finer in texture, orange-brown, pinkish-brown or medium reddish-brown, toning down to a pleasing golden-brown shade. It is generally considered to be less ornamental than Andaman padauk, though it sometimes shows a beautiful curled and mottled figure.

Seasoning and movement. The timber dries slowly without much degrade except for a tendency to develop fine surface checks. FPRL kiln schedule F is suggested. It is well known to be dimensionally stable in service.

Strength properties. One of the strongest and hardest timbers of South-East Asia; considerably stronger and harder than Andaman padauk and Burma teak.

Durability and preservative treatment. A very durable timber, highly resistant to fungi and insects, including termites. Extremely resistant to impregnation but preservative treatment is unnecessary.

Working and finishing properties. Difficult to saw, especially when dry, and hard to work but machines well, finishing with a smooth clean surface. In planing, the cutting angle should be reduced to 20°. The wood polishes well provided the grain is properly filled. It can be glued satisfactorily.

Uses. The value of Burma padauk is primarily due to its outstanding strength, durability and stability in service. After teak it is the best all-round utility timber in South-East Asia and is preferred to teak for purposes where great strength is required. It is traditionally used for the wheels of carts and gun carriages, for the frames of boats, for oil presses, tool handles and house building. Other uses include parquet flooring, furniture and cabinet work.

Padauk, Burma

Flat cut

  Reproduced actual size

Paldao

[Dracontomelum dao]

Distribution and supplies. *Dracontomelum* is widely distributed in South-East Asia and the South-West Pacific islands. The Philippine species, known as paldao or dao, is a tall tree up to 30 m. (100 ft.) or more in height, with a straight, clear stem above the buttresses. For many years there has been a small but regular export of veneer logs.

General description. A timber of particular interest because of its decorative, walnut-like appearance. Paldao more closely resembles 'Queensland walnut' than European walnut, having a greyish-brown wood with a greenish-yellow cast and irregular, dark-brown to almost black banding. Figured timber of this type is confined to the heartwood; the sapwood, which is sometimes very wide—as much as 200 mm. (8 in.) in small logs—is pale and featureless. The texture is medium and the grain interlocked or sometimes wavy, adding to the decorative appearance. When dry, the density is about 0·74 (46 lb./ft.^{3}), i.e. marginally heavier than European walnut and 'Queensland walnut'.

Technical properties. Like many decorative woods, particularly of the walnut type, paldao is used mainly in the form of veneer. It can be successfully rotary-peeled but is more usually sliced; the veneer glues satisfactorily, takes a good finish and polishes well.

Other technical properties are of relatively minor importance and such information as is available for the solid timber is based mainly on Philippine experience. On drying, it is reputed to have a moderate shrinkage with a tendency to warp and twist. It is rated a fairly strong wood, notably in toughness and bending, but has only moderate durability under conditions favouring decay; it is neither siliceous nor gummy and should present no undue difficulty in working, although care may be necessary when machining quartered surfaces if interlocked grain is present.

Uses. Paldao is one of the more attractive woods with a walnut-like appearance and, as veneer, is suitable in place of walnut for high-grade furniture and cabinet work, shop fitting, panelling and similar purposes.

Other species of interest. *Closely allied to paldao and virtually indistinguishable is 'New Guinea walnut', also known as 'Pacific walnut', 'Papuan walnut' and loup, of New Guinea and neighbouring islands. Three species of* Dracontomelum *have been recorded in Sabah; the local name is sengkuang. The figured heartwood, which is found only in certain trees, resembles paldao and 'New Guinea walnut' in appearance but is lighter in weight, average density about 0·59 (37 lb./ft.^{3}), seasoned. It is of interest as an alternative to true walnut.*

Paldao

Quarter cut

Reproduced actual size

Punah

[Tetramerista glabra]

Distribution and supplies. Punah is the Malay name for *Tetramerista glabra*, a large tree of the coastal swamp forests of the Malay Peninsula. The same or a closely allied species is found in Sumatra and Borneo, including Sabah and Sarawak. The timber is of some importance locally in Malaya where logs of 750 mm. (30 in.) diameter are quite common. Small quantities have been exported to Britain.

General description. A timber of plain appearance, straw-coloured or light-brown, sometimes tinged with pink, the rays standing out on quarter-sawn surfaces as orange-brown flecks. The grain is not generally interlocked but is sometimes spiral; the texture moderately coarse and even. Average density is about 0·70 (44 lb./ft.^{3}), seasoned.

Seasoning and movement. The timber dries rapidly under favourable conditions but requires care in seasoning to minimise splitting and cupping. It is not particularly stable and is liable to distort in use.

Strength properties. The results of standard tests indicate that punah is stronger than English oak except in shock resistance and it is less hard.

Durability and preservative treatment. Being only moderately resistant to decay, the timber is unsuitable for use in contact with the ground without preservative treatment. It is moderately resistant to impregnation.

Working and finishing properties. Punah can be sawn and planed without difficulty but requires considerable sanding to obtain a smooth finish. It takes nails reasonably well in large dimensions but thin boards are liable to split.

Uses. Punah is a general-utility timber, suitable for building work under cover.

Punah

Flat cut

 Reproduced actual size

Pyinkado

[Xylia xylocarpa]

Distribution and supplies. Pyinkado is widely distributed in Burma, as a large tree with a straight cylindrical bole. Squares up to 9 m. (30 ft.) long and 400 mm. (16 in.) side measurement are reported to be available in quantity for local use and for export and larger sizes can be supplied if required. It is common in parts of India also, especially the forests of the west coast where it is known as irul or jamba. Here the tree is not so large as in Burma.

General description. The heartwood is of plain appearance, dull reddish-brown with darker markings, very hard and heavy, with a density of nearly 1·0 (62 lb./ft.^{3}), seasoned. The grain is inclined to be irregular; the texture is moderately fine and even.

Seasoning and movement. The timber dries slowly but without serious degrade. Dimensional movement in service is classed as medium.

Strength properties. An exceptionally hard, heavy timber with correspondingly high strength, superior to teak but not equal to greenheart.

Durability and preservative treatment. The heartwood resists the attack of fungi, insects, including soil-burrowing termites, and marine borers and is classed as very durable. It is extremely resistant to preservative treatment.

Working and finishing properties. In the seasoned condition the wood is extremely difficult to work and rapidly blunts cutting edges. It should be sawn green. With care it can be finished to a smooth surface.

Uses. Pyinkado is pre-eminently a timber for heavy construction such as bridge building, marine piling and harbour work. After teak it is the most important timber in Burma for this class of work and for railway sleepers, for which it is claimed to be one of the best timbers in the world. It has been exported to Europe for harbour work and similar purposes. As flooring it wears as well as maple and is equally suitable where a good appearance is required and for heavy pedestrian and industrial traffic, as in warehouses and factories.

Pyinkado

Flat cut

Reproduced two-thirds actual size

Ramin

[Gonystylus bancanus]

Distribution and supplies. Ramin is a tall tree with a straight, clear, unbuttressed bole, 18 m. (60 ft.) in length but usually only about 0·6 m. (2 ft.) in diameter. It occurs in swamp forests and has a wide distribution in South-East Asia from Malaya, through parts of Sumatra to the west coast of Borneo and the Philippines, but it is in the peat swamps of the river deltas of Sarawak, notably the Rajang delta, that the trees occur in abundance and have been so extensively exploited. The timber is shipped mainly in the form of lumber, 19–50 mm. ($\frac{3}{4}$–2 in.) thick, up to 250 or 300 mm. (10 or 12 in.) wide, in lengths of about 5 m. (16–18 ft.) and as strips. Logs are up to 0·5 m. (2 ft.) in diameter and 6 m. (20 ft.) long. Supplies from Malaya may be invoiced and sold as melawis.

General description. The attraction of ramin lies in a combination of characteristics which make it a mild, easily handled, almost featureless, general-purpose timber. The uniformly coloured, creamy-white wood has a fine, even texture combined with a straight or only shallowly interlocked grain; it is almost devoid of any decorative feature, though occasional logs have wavy grain and yield figured wood. Ramin is of medium density, about 0·66 (41 lb./ft.^{3}) seasoned, i.e. a little lighter than beech and about the same as a mild grade of birch.

Freshly sawn logs have an unpleasant smell which may be very marked during kiln seasoning; it normally disappears once the timber is dry but there is a risk of its recurrence if the wood is wetted.

Seasoning and movement. Ramin seasons readily with little distortion or deterioration apart from a tendency to end-splitting and surface checking. FPRL kiln schedule C is usually recommended but an initial high temperature/high humidity treatment may be advisable to prevent fungal discoloration in the early stages of drying.

The wood has a moderate shrinkage when dried from green to 12 per moisture content. Dimensional movement under changes of humidity can be fairly large, approaching that of beech, and there is a definite tendency to check.

Strength and bending properties. Ramin compares favourably with beech in most of its strength properties but although somewhat superior in compression it is inferior in toughness, hardness and resistance to splitting. It is not recommended for solid bending.

Durability and preservative treatment. Ramin is particularly susceptible to deterioration by pinhole borers and staining fungi unless rapidly extracted, converted and given a combined fungicidal and insecticidal dip. It is classed as perishable but is readily treated with preservatives.

Working and finishing properties. Ramin can again be likened to medium-density beech in its resistance to working with hand and machine tools, causing only moderate blunting, and in planing and moulding finishes smoothly on flat-sawn surfaces; for quarter-sawn stock with strongly interlocked grain it may be advisable to reduce the cutting angle to 20°. It does not turn so well as beech; the finished surface is somewhat fibrous. There is some tendency to split on nailing and pre-boring is advisable. With its clear, pale colour ramin takes stain well and polishes to give a good finish.

Uses. Ramin was first shipped to Europe in the early 1950s; it quickly attracted interest and became established on the British market. It is largely used for furniture, mouldings, brush and broom handles and toys. For furniture manufacture it is generally purchased in the form of strips for use in small sections.

Ramin

Quarter cut

Reproduced actual size

Rosewood, Indian

[Dalbergia latifolia]

Distribution and supplies. Indian rosewood or Bombay blackwood is widely distributed in India, though nowhere very common. It is exported in limited quantities, mainly from South India. Logs may be as much as 1·5 m. (5 ft.) in diameter, though the average size is between 0·6 and 0·9 m. (2–3 ft.) diameter. This species is also found in Java.

General description. The heartwood is typically streaked, dark purplish-brown to nearly black, darker in colour than Brazilian rosewood but otherwise similar in general character, though the grain tends to be interlocked. The average density in the seasoned condition is about 0·85 (53 lb./ft.³).

Seasoning and movement. This timber is reported to be one of the few Indian hardwoods which air seasons better in the log or in rough squares than when converted green; also it retains its natural colour better when seasoned in this way. After conversion it should be kiln dried slowly to prevent splitting and checking. The colour is said to be improved by kiln seasoning; FPRL kiln schedule E is recommended. Once seasoned it absorbs moisture slowly and is dimensionally stable in service.

Strength properties. A strong timber, particularly hard for its weight, about 20 per cent harder than greenheart. Its other strength properties are rather better than those of oak and teak.

Durability. A very durable timber, highly resistant to decay and rarely attacked by termites. It does not require preservative treatment.

Working and finishing properties. Being very hard, it is difficult to work and has a considerable dulling effect on cutting edges, especially when chalky deposits are present. A good finish is obtained under normal working conditions. In planing, a cutting angle of 25° is recommended. The wood takes a high polish but the grain requires filling.

Uses. In Britain Indian rosewood is used mainly for high-class furniture, often in the form of veneer, and for musical instruments and small turned articles. In India, by virtue of its outstanding strength and durability it is also used for a wide range of constructional work.

Other species of interest. *The principal rosewood of Burma* (D. oliveri) *has been marketed as Burma tulipwood. Thailand rosewood, known as chin chan, is believed to be* D. cochinchinensis.

Rosewood, Indian

Quarter cut

Reproduced actual size

Sal

[Shorea robusta]

Distribution and supplies. Sal is one of the more important timbers of India. It is the principal species in a belt of forest running along the foothills of the Himalayas and in other large areas south of the Ganges. It is a large, well-formed tree. Squared logs may be as much as 15 m. (50 ft.) long with a 600 mm. (24 in.) side, the average size being about 4·5–6·0 m. (say, 15–20 ft.) long and 300–350 mm. (12–14 in.) in side measurement. Large supplies are available in North India

General description. This is a typical member of the group of *Shorea* species with heavy yellowish-brown wood, known as balau in Malaya and as selangan batu in Sabah, as distinct from the light- to medium-weight timbers of the meranti/seraya/lauan group. The heartwood is of plain appearance with a dull surface, darkening in time to reddish-brown. The grain is typically interlocked, giving a conspicuous stripe figure to quarter-sawn material. The weight varies considerably; density is mostly in the range 0·80–0·88 (50–55 lb./ft.^{3}), seasoned.

Seasoning and movement. Except in small dimensions the timber dries very slowly with a tendency to surface checking and end-splitting, though distortion is not serious provided the timber is properly stacked. Kiln drying is probably economic only for boards up to about 40 mm. ($1\frac{1}{2}$ in.) thick. Experience with other timbers of this group suggests that FPRL kiln schedule G may be suitable. Dimensional movement in service is about average.

Strength properties. Sal is appreciably stronger than teak and about twice as hard.

Durability and preservative treatment. In India sal heartwood is rated highly durable. It is virtually impermeable to liquids but the sapwood is permeable and preservative treatment of round posts and poles is recommended.

Working and finishing properties. In the dry condition sal is difficult to saw and work. It is usually sawn green. It cuts cleanly in most operations. To minimise tearing on quarter-sawn surfaces the cutting angle should be reduced to 20°.

Uses. Sal is essentially a timber for heavy constructional purposes where strength and durability are the main requirements. In India and Pakistan it is largely used for railway sleepers and such work as bridging, piling, house building, wagon building and vats. It has little to commend it for export overseas.

Other species of interest. *Burma sal or ingyin (S. obtusa) is in general similar to Indian sal. Other timbers in this group are chan (Thailand), balau (Malaya), selangan batu (Sabah), alan (Sarawak and Brunei) and guijo (Philippines). They may be considered broadly equivalent to Indian sal and suitable for the same purposes. Since the number of species included in the group is of the order of 30 or more there is considerable variation in technical properties, notably in resistance to fungus and insect attack.*

Sal

Flat cut

Reproduced actual size

FO

Satinwood, East Indian

[Chloroxylon swietenia]

Distribution and supplies. East Indian or Ceylon satinwood is a fairly common tree in Central and South India and in Ceylon, where it attains its maximum size of about 0·9 m. (3 ft.) in diameter. Ceylon is the main source of supply. Logs for export are 300–900 mm. (12–36 in.) in diameter, 1·8–7·5 m. (6–25 ft.) long, nearly all more or less figured.

General description. A remarkably handsome, golden-yellow to golden-brown wood with no clear distinction between sapwood and heartwood, though wood from near the centre of large logs tends to be darker. It resembles West Indian satinwood but is more highly figured, with a wider range of colour. The texture is fine and even; the grain irregularly interlocked. Quarter-cut material presents an exceptionally beautiful figure—ribbon grain, broken stripe or mottle—enhanced by the satin lustre of the wood. It is very hard and heavy (heavier than West Indian satinwood), average density about 0·98 (61 lb./ft.^{3}), seasoned.

Technical properties. Satinwood seasons well with care. FPRL kiln schedule C is recommended. Accurate strength figures are not available but the timber is known to be much stronger than teak and slightly harder than greenheart. Under tropical conditions it is extremely durable. It is hard to work by both hand and machine tools and has a considerable dulling effect on cutting edges. The irregular grain makes it liable to pick up in planing, especially on quarter-sawn surfaces; the cutting angle should be reduced to 15°. The wood finishes cleanly in most other operations and turns very well, taking a fine polish from the tool.

Uses. In India and Ceylon, by virtue of its outstanding strength and durability, satinwood has long been used for a wide range of constructional and utility work as well as for ornamental purposes. In Europe it became popular in the nineteenth century for cabinet work and high-class furniture and fittings. Latterly it has been used to a limited extent for its decorative qualities in small items such as brush backs and handles for toilet accessories. Because of its excellent technical qualities it has been found suitable for the heads of croquet mallets and for certain musical instruments, notably recorders.

Satinwood, East Indian

Quarter cut

 Reproduced actual size

Sen

[principally *Kalopanax pictus,* formerly known as *Acanthopanax ricinifolius*]

Distribution and supplies. Sen is a timber of some importance in Japan. The tree commonly grows to a height of 24 m. (80 ft.) and a diameter of 1 m. (3 ft. or more). The timber was introduced to the United Kingdom market in the 1930s as plywood and square-sawn material and has also been shipped in log form for cutting into veneer.

General description. In general appearance sen has a strong resemblance to a soft type of ash, being light greyish-brown with a prominent growth-ring figure on plywood and flat-sawn timber. It is considerably lighter and softer than the general run of European or American ash, however, the average density being about 0·56 (35 lb./ft.^{3}), seasoned. The wood is typically straight grained.

Seasoning and movement. The timber presents no special difficulty in seasoning. It is not particularly stable in use.

Strength properties. Compared with European ash and American white ash of average quality, sen is inferior in all strength properties. It is more nearly comparable to American whitewood (yellow poplar) in this respect.

Durability and preservative treatment. It is classed as non-durable. Preservative treatment is recommended for railway sleepers though the wood is fairly resistant to impregnation.

Working and finishing properties. The wood is easy to work but is inclined to be brittle. It is readily peeled and sliced for plywood and decorative veneer.

Uses. In Japan sen is used for a wide range of purposes where no great strength or durability is required. On the world market it is better known as plywood for interior use and as decorative veneer.

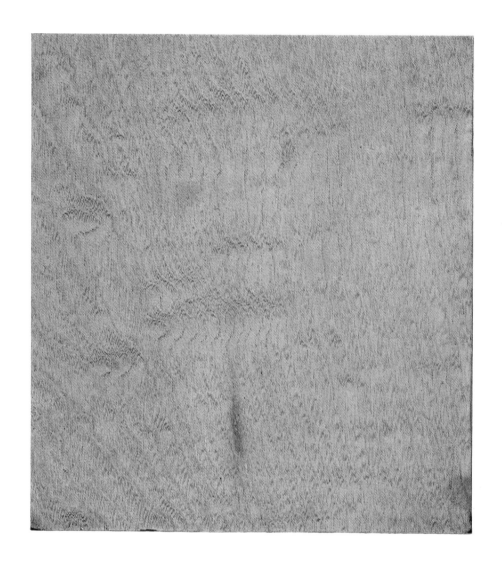

Sen

Flat cut

Reproduced actual size

Sepetir

[Pseudosindora palustris and various species of *Sindora]*

Distribution and supplies. The Malay name sepetir has been adopted as the British Standard name for the timber of *Pseudosindora palustris* and closely allied species of *Sindora*, widely distributed and locally common in South-East Asia. The trees may be 1 m. or more (say, 4 ft.) in diameter but are usually much smaller. The timber is known to be available commercially in Malaya, Sabah and Sarawak. Selected material has been exported in small quantities.

General description. The sapwood is unusually wide, clearly differentiated from the heartwood which is variable in character (depending on the species), the colour ranging from light-brown or pinkish to dark-brown or reddish-brown, with darker markings. In some logs the prevailing shade is reddish, in others the wood is finely figured with dark-brown or black streaks, suggesting walnut. The general effect can be highly decorative, particularly in flat-sawn material or rotary-cut veneer. The texture is moderately fine and even, the grain usually straight. The average density is of the order of 0·67 (42 lb./ft.^{3}), seasoned.

Seasoning and movement. The timber dries slowly with a tendency to develop end splits but with little distortion. FPRL kiln schedule G has given good results. Dimensional movement of seasoned timber in service is small.

Strength and bending properties. The results of tests on a consignment of *P. palustris* from Sarawak indicate that the timber is approximately equal to English oak in shock resistance and toughness and superior in bending and compression strength, stiffness, shear and hardness. It is classed as moderately good for steam bending.

Durability and preservative treatment. Reports on durability are conflicting. The heartwood is probably durable under European conditions. It is extremely resistant to preservative treatment (*P. palustris*).

Working and finishing properties. The timber is fairly hard to work; the blunting effect on cutting edges is comparable to that of English oak. It finishes cleanly in most operations and takes an excellent polish.

Uses. Sepetir is of value mainly for furniture and cabinet work, in the solid and as veneer. Owing to the width of the sapwood conversion losses are high; furthermore, careful selection is necessary to obtain well-figured material. Boards should be flat-sawn and veneers rotary-cut to show the figure to the best advantage.

Sepetir

Flat cut

Reproduced actual size

Seraya, White

[species of *Parashorea*]

Distribution and supplies. Timber of the white seraya type is produced by two species of *Parashorea* and is available commercially only from Sabah (where it is known as urat mata) and the Philippines (local name bagtikan), although Indonesian Borneo is another potential source of supply. The trees grow to a very large size, up to about 60 m. (say, 200 ft.) in height, with a long, straight, cylindrical bole up to nearly 2 m. (6–7 ft.) in diameter. The timber is exported from Sabah in large quantities, mainly to Japan, as logs for conversion to plywood.

General description. When freshly sawn the heartwood of white seraya is nearly white, sometimes with a pinkish tint; on exposure it darkens to a light yellowish-brown shade not always clearly demarcated from the sapwood. In grain and texture it resembles light red meranti/seraya but is more uniform in character. The average density is about 0·53 (33 lb./ft.^{3}) in the seasoned condition, i.e. about the same as African mahogany. Brittleheart is commonly present.

Seasoning and movement. The timber seasons fairly well with some distortion but with little tendency to check or split. FPRL kiln schedule J is recommended. The movement of seasoned timber in service is classed as small.

Strength and bending properties. White seraya is similar to African mahogany in strength. It is considered unsuitable for solid bending.

Durability and preservative treatment. Non-durable and extremely resistant to preservative treatment.

Working and finishing properties. The timber works fairly easily with little blunting effect on cutting edges. A clean finish is obtained in most machining operations provided sharp, thin-edged tools are employed. It takes stains well and can be glued satisfactorily.

Uses. White seraya is primarily a plywood timber. The sawn timber has been utilised successfully in the United Kingdom for ships' decking, in place of teak, also for joinery and light structural work.

Other species of interest. *Other species of* Parashorea *occur elsewhere in South-East Asia; their timbers are harder and heavier than white seraya and have attracted little commercial interest. White meranti (certain species of* Shorea, *see p. 56) is not the same as white seraya.*

Seraya, White

Quarter cut

 Reproduced actual size

Teak

[Tectona grandis]

Tectona grandis is the only true teak. It should not be confused with certain other timbers, such as the so-called Borneo teak, Brunei teak and 'Rhodesian teak', which have some of the characteristics of teak but are quite distinct.

Distribution and supplies. Teak is indigenous in India, Burma, Thailand and Vietnam and is virtually naturalised in Java and some of the smaller islands of the Indonesian Archipelago. It is also grown successfully in certain other countries where climatic conditions are suitable, notably Ceylon, Nigeria (mainly for poles and fuel) and Trinidad. The first shipments of teak to Europe were made from the west coast of India (the Malabar Coast). Later came the development of the teak trade in Burma (Moulmein teak), Java and Thailand. Nowadays Burma and Thailand are the main sources of supply for the world market. The timber is available as round logs, 300–500 mm. (12–20 in.) or more in diameter, up to 9 m. (30 ft.) in length, or more commonly as squared logs, as square-edged material in a wide range of sizes, 12–200 mm. ($\frac{1}{2}$–8 in.) thick, 75–375 mm. (3–15 in.) wide, 0·9–5·5 m. (3–18 ft.) long, and as ships' decking and veneer.

General description. Teak has a characteristic golden-brown colour, darkening in time, sometimes with irregular dark markings which enhance the appearance of the wood. The freshly machined surface can be remarkably variable in colour, with unsightly blotches and streaks, but after a short period of exposure to light and air it tones down to the familiar golden-brown shade. After prolonged exposure to the weather, however, as in ships' decking and garden furniture, teak bleaches to very light grey. The grain is typically straight but some logs have irregular grain and these are generally selected for conversion to veneer for decorative work. The texture is rather coarse, due to the ring-porous structure. The wood contains an oleo-resin and has a characteristic smell which has been likened to that of old leather. On average it is slightly lighter than oak, the density being about 0·66 (41 lb./ft.^{3}), seasoned.

Seasoning and movement. Teak seasons well, though rather slowly and irregularly due to unusually large variations in moisture content and drying rate. FPRL kiln schedule H has given good results. The stability of teak in service is well known. Dimensional movement is classed as small.

Strength and bending properties. Teak has good all-round strength properties, being similar to English oak in most respects. Like oak, very slowly grown, narrow-ringed wood is apt to be brittle. Bending qualities are variable and teak is not recommended for solid bentwork.

Durability and preservative treatment. Teak is highly resistant to fungal and insect attack, including termites, and is classed as very durable. It is attacked by *Teredo* in the Rangoon River but is usually found to be resistant to marine borers in temperate waters. It is impermeable to liquids but is not a timber which requires preservative treatment.

Working and finishing properties. Teak works reasonably well with hand and machine tools but cutting edges are soon dulled, due to the silica content, unless special wear-resistant tools are used. A good finish is obtainable provided tools are kept sharp and care is exercised in working the end grain, which is inclined to be brittle. A freshly worked surface often feels rather rough, however, due to the texture

[continued on page 92]

Teak

Flat cut

Reproduced actual size

Quarter cut

TEAK [*continued from page 90*]

and oily nature of the wood. Teak takes nails and screws fairly well. For gluing, the surface should be freshly machined or sanded.

Uses. Teak is world famous for its durability and stability, combined with good strength and working properties and pleasing appearance. Recognition of its outstanding qualities for ship building led to the development of the teak trade in the nineteenth century and it is still considered one of the best timbers for this purpose, though its use is limited by the high price. Its main use in ship and boat building is for decking; it is also used for planking, especially for boats in tropical waters, and for deckhouses and fittings. In other fields of usage in Britain teak is normally reserved for special purposes, notably high-class joinery, especially outside work such as doors, window frames, greenhouses and garden furniture (for which it needs no paint or varnish to protect it), for laboratory bench tops and industrial chemical plant, on account of its resistance to acids, and for flooring, especially where subfloor heating is installed. Since the second world war it has become popular for furniture and cabinet work, in the solid and as veneer. In the countries of origin teak is the standard timber for all kinds of constructional work.

Figured Teak

Flat cut

Reproduced actual size

Walnut, Japanese

[*Juglans sieboldiana*]

Distribution and supplies. Japanese walnut is reported to be a fairly common tree in Hokkaido, the north island of Japan, where it attains a height of about 20 m. (65 ft.) and a diameter of 1 m. (3 ft. or more). The timber has been marketed in Britain as the face veneer of decorative plywood under the name of Japanese claro or claro walnut.

General description. Like European walnut, logs show three zones—sapwood, true heartwood and an intermediate zone. The true heartwood is golden-brown or pinkish-brown, more or less streaked, typically lighter in colour than European walnut and considerably lighter in weight, the average density being about 0·43 (27 lb./ft.^{3}), seasoned, resembling American butternut or white walnut.

Technical properties. The timber is known to have excellent working and finishing properties, resembling in these respects the better-known walnut woods of Europe and North America, but is considerably softer and inferior in strength. It is reputed to be stable in service.

Uses. Japanese walnut is used for furniture, interior joinery and decorative panelling.

94

Walnut, Japanese

Flat cut

  Reproduced actual size

Asian Timbers
SOFTWOODS

Deodar

[Cedrus deodara]

Distribution and supplies. Deodar is found in the Himalayan region where it grows to a very large size and attains a great age. The average diameter of mature trees is about 1·0 m. (say, 3–4 ft.). It is the most important timber of North India. Very large quantities are extracted from the forests as logs, railway sleepers and scantlings and floated down the rivers to the plains. The timber is not normally exported but the tree is planted for ornamental purposes in Europe and America.

General description. The heartwood is strongly scented and resinous, of plain appearance, light-brown with a rather dull surface; generally straight grained with a fairly fine, even texture, with little contrast between the spring wood and summer wood zones. In the seasoned condition the density is about 0·56 (35 lb./ft.^{3}).

Seasoning. The timber can be dried without difficulty, with the minimum of splitting and warping, except in badly grown material which is rare.

Strength properties. Deodar is similar to Baltic redwood in bending strength and stiffness and is appreciably harder but is inclined to be brittle.

Durability and preservative treatment. The heartwood is rarely attacked by fungi or insects, including termites, even when in contact with the ground, and is classed as durable. It resists impregnation and it is doubtful whether preservative treatment would prolong the life of deodar sleepers.

Working and finishing properties. The wood is easy to work by hand or with machine tools and has little dulling effect on cutting edges. It takes a moderately good matt finish; the surface is inclined to be sticky when freshly cut, due to the oleo-resin content.

Uses. Deodar is largely used in India and Pakistan for railway sleepers and in building, for both structural work and joinery. Other uses include roofing shingles, railway carriages and wagons, boxes and packing cases.

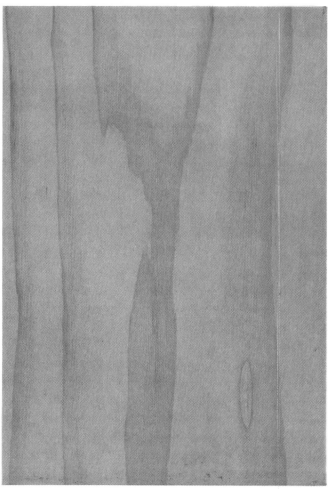

Deodar

Quarter cut

Reproduced actual size

Flat cut

Sugi or Japanese Cedar

[*Cryptomeria japonica*]

Description and supplies. Sugi is the most important timber tree of Japan, where it forms some 30 per cent of the forest area; it also occurs in China. A large tree attaining a height of 45 m. (150 ft.) or more and a diameter of 1·5 m. (5 ft.) or more with a clean tapering trunk.

General description. The heartwood is light reddish-brown to purplish-brown, resembling western red cedar or California redwood in general character, with a pleasant fragrance. The texture is fine to coarse, depending on the width of the rings which are strongly marked by the contrasting bands of spring wood and summer wood and give the timber a decorative appearance, especially when flat-sawn. It is typically straight grained and exceptionally light in weight, average density about 0·40 (25 lb./ft.^{3}), seasoned.

Technical properties. The timber can be dried without difficulty and is exceptionally stable. Being unusually light in weight, even for a softwood, it is not particularly strong. It is reported to be moderately durable and is easy to work, taking a good finish.

Uses. Sugi is one of the most widely used timbers of Japan. Uses there include all kinds of building construction, joinery, panelling, furniture, boxes, etc. It is seldom seen in Europe or USA, except in manufactured articles.

100

Sugi or Japanese Cedar

Flat cut

Reproduced actual size

Australian Timbers
HARDWOODS

Beech, Myrtle

[Nothofagus cunninghamii]

Distribution and supplies. *Nothofagus* is the beech of the Southern Hemisphere, an important genus in the temperate zone of South America, Australia and New Zealand. Myrtle beech, also known as Tasmanian myrtle, Tasmanian beech or simply myrtle or beech, is the principal Australian species. It is found in Tasmania and Victoria as a large tree up to 30 m. or even 60 m. (say, 100–200 ft.) in height and up to 1–1·5 m. (say, 3–5 ft.) in diameter. The timber is commonly available in Australia in the form of lumber, turnery squares and plywood.

General description. A medium-density hardwood of plain appearance, resembling the closely allied New Zealand silver beech but heavier; average density about 0·71 (44 lb./ft.^{3}), seasoned. It also resembles Northern Hemisphere beech and birch but lacks the characteristic large rays of true beech. The colour ranges from white in the sapwood to pink or reddish-brown in the heart, commonly with a wide transition zone. It is customary to sort the timber into two classes, 'white' and 'red'. The grain is typically straight or slightly interlocked; the texture fine and even.

Seasoning. The lighter-coloured 'white' timber dries fairly readily with little degrade but the 'red' requires careful control of drying conditions to minimise internal and surface checking and collapse. FPRL kiln schedule C after preliminary air drying is recommended.

Strength and bending properties. Definite information on strength is not available. The timber is probably similar to European beech and birch in most respects. It is one of the best Australian timbers for steam bending.

Durability and preservative treatment. The timber is classed as non-durable. The 'white' wood is permeable, the 'red' probably impermeable and resistant to preservative treatment.

Working and finishing properties. The timber can be worked fairly readily to a good finish in most hand and machine operations, being similar to European beech in this respect. It is excellent for turning and can be glued satisfactorily.

Uses. Myrtle beech is suitable for much the same purposes as European beech. Typical uses in Australia are furniture, general turnery, brushes and brooms, flooring and plywood.

Other species of interest. *Negrohead beech or Antarctic beech (*N. moorei*), of New South Wales and Queensland, is similar to myrtle beech and is used for the same purposes.*

Beech, Myrtle

Flat cut

Reproduced actual size

Black Bean

[Castanospermum australe]

Distribution and supplies. Black bean is sparsely distributed in New South Wales and Queensland. Under favourable conditions it attains a height of 37 m. (120 ft.) and a diameter of about 1 m. (3 ft. 3 in.), the bole length being up to two-thirds the height of the tree. Logs average 0·7–0·9 m. (28–36 in.) diameter. Heart shake is a common defect and the sapwood is unusually wide so the yield on conversion is little more than one-third of the measured log volume. The timber is available in small quantities as boards and in joinery sizes, as veneers and veneered panels for flush doors, etc.

General description. The ornamental character of the wood is due to the chocolate-brown background being relieved by the lighter-coloured tissue surrounding the pores. The grain is usually straight but may be interlocked; the texture is rather coarse and uneven, greasy to the touch. The general effect is similar to walnut. The wood is slightly heavier than walnut, the average density being about 0·70 (44 lb./ft.^{3}), seasoned.

Seasoning and movement. To minimise degrade in the shape of collapse, honeycombing and splitting, the timber should be air-dried slowly under cover before being kilned and finally reconditioned to remove collapse. FPRL kiln schedule C is suggested. Dimensional movement in use is medium.

Strength and bending properties. Precise information is lacking but the timber is considered to be moderately strong and stiff and inclined to be brittle. It is unsuitable for steam bending.

Durability. Black bean is durable in the ground and resistant to termites.

Working and finishing properties. The wood is slightly difficult to work but easier than 'Queensland walnut', with less dulling effect on tools. A clean finish can be obtained under ordinary working conditions. It slices well and is considered a good wood for carving.

Uses. Black bean is essentially a decorative wood, used mainly for high-class furniture, panelling, carving and fancy articles. Because of its good insulating properties it is suitable for switchboards and electrical fittings.

Black Bean

Quarter cut

   Reproduced two-thirds actual size

Blackbutt

[Eucalyptus pilularis]

Distribution and supplies. Blackbutt is one of the more important timber trees of Eastern Australia. It is a common constituent of the coastal forests of New South Wales and Queensland, where it grows to a height of 45 m. (150 ft.) or more with a clear bole up to two-thirds of the total height. The diameter seldom exceeds 1 m. (3 ft. 3 in.). The timber is readily available locally in a wide range of sizes. This species is grown successfully in plantations in other parts of the world.

General description. The colour is light-brown to brown, with a pinkish tinge when freshly cut. The wood is only moderately heavy by Australian standards, average density about 0·88 (55 lb./ft.^{3}), seasoned. It has a moderately fine texture with a straight or occasionally interlocked or wavy grain and is of plain appearance. Small gum veins are a characteristic feature.

Seasoning. The timber is liable to check in drying, particularly flat-sawn material, and collapse may occur. Air seasoning prior to kiln treatment (FPRL kiln schedule C) is advised except in the case of thin stock, which can be kiln dried satisfactorily from the green condition.

Strength and bending properties. In the Australian classification of structural timbers blackbutt is included in Group B. It is similar to karri in most strength properties but is not quite so hard and is easier to split. It is moderately good for steam bending.

Durability and preservative treatment. Blackbutt is classed as moderately durable in Australia and as durable under European conditions. It is extremely resistant to preservative treatment.

Working and finishing properties. Though fairly hard, the wood can be worked without difficulty with hand and machine tools and generally takes a good finish under normal machining conditions. If the grain is irregular it may be advisable to reduce the cutting angle to about 15°. Gluing is satisfactory.

Uses. In Australia blackbutt is regarded as a useful timber for general construction. It is largely used in housebuilding for carcassing, weather boarding, flooring and general carpentry, also for railway coaches, sleepers, bridge planking, transmission poles, cross-arms, split rails and posts for fencing, paving blocks and wood wool.

Other species of interest. *Western Australian blackbutt (E. patens) is a timber of minor importance, used locally for general construction, railway wagons, sleepers and packing cases.*

Blackbutt

Flat cut

Reproduced actual size

Blackwood, Australian or Tasmanian

[Acacia melanoxylon]

Distribution and supplies. This well-known tree is fairly widely distributed in New South Wales and Victoria and reaches its best development in Tasmania, where it attains a height of 25–30 m. (80–100 ft.) and a diameter of nearly 1 m. (say, 3 ft.). The timber is available in Australia in the form of split staves, sawn material and plain or fancy veneer. It is occasionally exported as sliced veneers or as solid timber.

General description. The name blackwood is misleading, the prevailing colour varying from golden-brown to dark-brown with narrow, nearly black bands marking the growth rings. The grain is usually straight but sometimes interlocked or wavy, giving rise to a highly decorative fiddleback figure, generally associated with a natural lustre. The texture is medium and even. The average density is about 0·66 (41 lb./ft.³), seasoned.

Seasoning. The timber can be air-dried or kiln-dried without difficulty and with little degrade. FPRL kiln schedule E is suggested.

Strength and bending properties. Precise information is not available but the timber is known to have relatively high strength properties and is good for steam bending.

Durability. The heartwood is believed to be durable though it is not normally used in situations exposed to decay or insect attack.

Working and finishing properties. The timber is easily worked with hand and machine tools, finishing to a smooth surface which takes a high polish. A reduction of the cutting angle to 20° is advisable when planing figured material.

Uses. Blackwood is one of the most highly valued Australian timbers for interior joinery. Because of its good bending qualities it is also used for bentwork in coach building, boat building and furniture. Plain straight-grained material makes excellent staves for beer casks. This species has been used in Britain for panelling and interior work in public buildings and railway coaches.

Blackwood, Australian or Tasmanian
Quarter cut

  Reproduced two-thirds actual size

Brush Box

[Tristania conferta]

Distribution and supplies. Brush box is an important tree of the coastal forests of Eastern Australia. It varies in size, depending on soil conditions; at its best it grows to a height of 40 m. (130 ft.) and a basal diameter of 1·5 m. (5 ft.). The timber is in good supply, in boards and structural sizes.

General description. A heavy structural timber of plain appearance, resembling turpentine in general character. Brown or reddish-brown, turning grey on exposure to the weather, with a fine, even texture and irregularly interlocked grain. Average density about 0·90 (56 lb./ft.^{3}), seasoned.

Seasoning and movement. Severe distortion can be expected in seasoning and flat-sawn material is liable to check. Air drying to a moisture content of 30 per cent or less is recommended as a preliminary to kiln seasoning (FPRL kiln schedule C followed by a reconditioning treatment). Once seasoned the timber is reported to keep its shape well.

Strength and bending properties. In the Australian classification of structural timbers brush box is placed in Group B. It has particularly good wearing qualities, withstanding rough usage without splintering. It is unsuitable for steam bending.

Durability and preservative treatment. The timber is only moderately durable, being inferior to turpentine in this respect. The heartwood is extremely resistant to preservative treatment.

Working and finishing properties. The timber is fairly hard to work with either hand or machine tools but has less dulling effect than turpentine. A clean finish can be obtained in planing if the cutting angle is reduced to 20°. Though the timber is difficult to nail, pre-boring is not essential.

Uses. Brush box is regarded as the best Australian timber for bridge and wharf decking. It is also used for heavy-duty industrial flooring, for the heads of mauls and mallets and for a wide range of structural work.

Brush Box
Quarter cut

Reproduced actual size

Coachwood or Scented Satinwood

[Ceratopetalum apetalum]

Distribution and supplies. The tree is of medium size, attaining a height of about 30 m. (100 ft.) and a diameter of about 0·75 m. (2 ft. 6 in.). It is practically confined to New South Wales where the timber is available in reasonable quantities as sawn boards, squares, mouldings, veneers and plywood.

General description. The timber has a pleasing appearance, being light pinkish-brown with a straight grain, a fine, even texture and a delicate figure on flat-sawn surfaces. It has a distinctive scent which has been compared to that of new-mown hay. It is of medium density, average about 0·63 (39 lb./ft.³), seasoned.

Seasoning. The timber can be dried without difficulty in thicknesses up to 75 mm. (3 in.). There is little tendency to warp, but slight collapse may occur.

Strength properties. Coachwood has good strength properties for its weight. It is similar to European beech in most respects but is not so hard.

Durability. Coachwood is not a durable timber though it has the advantage of being immune to *Lyctus* attack. It is unsuitable for outdoor use.

Working and finishing properties. The wood is easily worked to a smooth, silky finish either by hand or machine tools. It turns well, is good for carving and is readily polished. Gluing is satisfactory.

Uses. Coachwood is used in Australia for a wide range of manufactured goods, including furniture and cabinet work, joinery and interior fittings and turnery. It makes a high-grade plywood suitable for aircraft and marine use. Rotary-cut veneers are also used for decorative work. It is the best Australian timber for rifle stocks.

Coachwood or Scented Satinwood
Flat cut

 Reproduced actual size

Gum, Southern Blue

[*Eucalyptus globulus* and *E. bicostata*]

In Australia the term gum is used loosely to mean any kind of *Eucalyptus*, of which over 500 species have been identified. In the strict sense of the term gum embraces a relatively small group, including between 30 and 40 species of more or less importance as timber.

Distribution and supplies. *Eucalyptus globulus* is found mainly in Tasmania. It is grown extensively in other parts of the world, in plantations for fuel, poles and timber production and as an ornamental or shade tree. In its natural habitat it reaches a height of 20–45 m. (65–150 ft.) and a diameter of 1–1·5 m. (say, 3–5 ft.). *E. bicostata* grows at higher altitudes in New South Wales and Victoria. The two species are considered to be identical so far as their timber is concerned. In Australia the annual production is comparatively small and supplies are difficult to obtain.

General description. The heartwood is light yellowish-brown (the term blue refers to the colour of the bark) with a fairly open texture. The grain is commonly interlocked, occasionally wavy, producing an attractive ripple figure, as illustrated. The average density of the Australian-grown timber is about 0·90 (56 lb./ft.^{3}), seasoned. Grown as an exotic it tends to be considerably lighter in weight.

Seasoning. The timber is fairly difficult to dry without degrade in the shape of checking and collapse. Quarter cutting is recommended and initial air-drying to 30 per cent moisture content is suggested before kilning.

Strength and bending properties. In the Australian classification of structural timbers, southern blue gum is included in Group B with such timbers as blackbutt, karri and turpentine. Selected material is good for steam bending.

Durability. The heartwood is classed as moderately durable, in the same category as blackbutt, karri and Sydney blue gum. It is resistant to marine borers.

Working and finishing properties. This timber is fairly difficult to work on account of its density and interlocked grain. However, with due care and attention to cutting tools a good machine finish can be obtained.

Uses. Southern blue gum is used in Australia for piles and wharf timbering, bridge building, vehicle body building and other structural purposes, also for cross-arms on telegraph poles and for pick, axe and hammer handles.

116

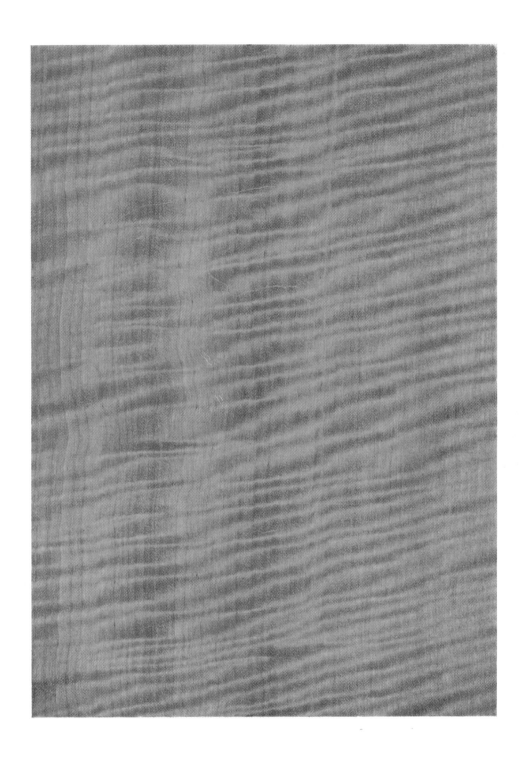

Gum, Southern Blue

Quarter cut

 Reproduced two-thirds actual size

Gum, Spotted

[*Eucalyptus maculata* and *E. citriodora*]

Distribution and supplies. Spotted gum is one of the best-known timbers in the coastal forests of Queensland and New South Wales. The trees grow to a height of 37 m. (120 ft.) with a diameter of 1 m. (3 ft. 3 in.) or more. The timber is available in large quantities and in a wide range of sizes. *Eucalyptus maculata* is cultivated as an exotic in other parts of the world.

General description. The heartwood is light-brown or greyish-brown to dark-brown, the sapwood distinctly lighter in colour. The texture is rather coarse, similar to that of oak except for the absence of pore rings. The grain may be straight, interlocked or wavy. The wood is slightly greasy. It is one of the heavier *Eucalyptus* timbers; the average density is about 1·01 (63 lb./ft.³), seasoned.

Seasoning. The timber needs to be dried carefully to minimise checking, distortion and collapse. Kiln drying from the green condition is not recommended.

Strength and bending properties. Because of its variability, spotted gum is placed in both Group A and Group B in the Australian classification of structural timbers. It is classed as good for steam bending.

Durability and preservative treatment. The heartwood is classed as moderately durable. It is extremely resistant to preservative treatment.

Working and finishing properties. Considering its density it is not difficult to work, being similar to European oak in its resistance to cutting and its dulling effect on tools. A good finish can generally be obtained, using a cutting angle of 20°–25°. The wood is too hard for nailing but takes screws fairly well.

Uses. Spotted gum is used in Australia for a wide range of constructional work where strength, hardness and shock-resistance are required, including bridge work, shipbuilding, agricultural machinery and the bent parts of railway coaches, also for flooring. It is the most satisfactory available Australian timber for the handles of axes, picks and shovels. In Britain it has been used for cross-arms for transmission and telegraph poles.

Gum, Spotted

Flat cut

Reproduced actual size

Gum, Sydney Blue

[Eucalyptus saligna]

Distribution and supplies. *Eucalyptus saligna* is one of the more important general construction timbers of New South Wales. In its natural habitat the tree attains a height of 40–50 m. (say, 130–160 ft.) with a straight, clear bole up to two-thirds of the total height, 1·2–1·8 m. (4–6 ft.) in diameter. It is grown extensively in plantations in other parts of the world, sometimes under the name of saligna gum. Except where otherwise stated, the following description refers to timber grown in Australia under forest conditions. This is available locally in a full range of standard sizes.

General description. The timber is typically rose-red but may vary from pink to a dark-red shade. The grain is usually straight or slightly interlocked but sometimes wavy, producing an attractive ripple figure. The texture is rather coarse. The average density is about 0·82 (51 lb./ft.^{3}), seasoned. When grown in plantations the wood is considerably lighter in weight; for example the density range for South African material is 0·48–0·62 (30–39 lb./ft.^{3}).

Seasoning. Quarter-sawn timber can be dried readily in the air or in a kiln with little degrade. Flat-sawn material is liable to check.

Strength properties. Sydney blue gum is described as a hard, stiff and tough timber, similar in strength to blackbutt and karri.

Durability. The heartwood is classed as moderately durable, being fairly resistant to decay and termite attack.

Working and finishing properties. Considering its density the wood is easy to work, nail, dress and finish and takes a good polish.

Uses. A general-purpose hardwood, largely used in Australia for structural work in building, flooring, weatherboarding and boat building. It is considered one of the best woods for roofing shingles.

Gum, Sydney Blue

Flat cut

Reproduced actual size

Ironbark

[various species of *Eucalyptus*]

The ironbarks of Australia fall into two main groups so far as their timber is concerned. Grey ironbark is the standard common name for the timber of *Eucalyptus paniculata* and *E. fergusoni*. The name red ironbark covers *E. sideroxylon*, *E. siderophloia* and *E. crebra*.

Distribution and supplies. The range of distribution of the various species includes Victoria, New South Wales and Queensland. The trees grow to a height of 24–30 m. (80–100 ft.) and a diameter of 0·6–0·9 m. (2–3 ft.). The timber is available in Australia in moderate quantity, in a wide range of sizes, as round, hewn and sawn material. *E. paniculata* is grown successfully in plantations, notably in South Africa, Rhodesia and Malawi.

General description. These constructional timbers are extremely hard and heavy; the average density is of the order of 1·12 (70 lb./ft.^{3}), seasoned. The colour of the heartwood varies according to the species from brown to reddish-brown or dark-red. The grain is generally interlocked, the texture moderately fine and even.

Seasoning. The timber dries very slowly and is liable to check. As it is generally used in large sizes for structural purposes, kiln drying is not generally practised. Flooring stock should be partially air dried before kiln drying to the final moisture content. FPRL kiln schedule B is suggested.

Strength properties. Ironbark is placed in Group A in the Australian classification of structural timbers. It is about equal to greenheart in bending strength, stiffness and compressive strength along the grain and about 30 per cent harder, but 50–60 per cent inferior in its resistance to splitting.

Durability and preservative treatment. All species of ironbark are included in Class 1 in the Australian classification of timbers according to their resistance to fungal decay and termite attack. They are less resistant to marine borer attack. The timber is almost impossible to impregnate with preservatives.

Working and finishing properties. The timber is hard to work in all machine operations and is extremely difficult to cut with hand tools. A smooth finish can be obtained on fairly straight-grained material under standard machining conditions but the cutting angle should be reduced to 15° when the grain is interlocked, as is usually the case.

Uses. The ironbarks are among the most valuable Australian timbers for heavy durable construction. They are used mainly for railway sleepers, piles, poles, bridge and wharf construction, also for house framing, railway wagons, ship building and flooring.

Ironbark

Flat cut

Reproduced actual size

Jarrah

[*Eucalyptus marginata*]

Distribution and supplies. Jarrah is a tree of Western Australia where it grows to a height of 30–45 m. (100–150 ft.), clear of branches to 12–18 m. (40–60 ft.), with a butt diameter of 1·0–1·5 m. (say, 3–5 ft.). Large quantities of the timber are available in a wide range of sizes and continuity of supplies is assured. Since production on a commercial scale was started 100 years ago jarrah has been shipped to all parts of the world. It is normally produced in thicknesses of 25–150 mm. (1–6 in.), widths of 75–300 mm. (3–12 in.), in lengths of 1·5–8·5 m. (5–28 ft.) and as manufactured flooring. The maximum dimensions quoted are 350 ×350 mm. (14 ×14 in.) and about 10·5 m. (35 ft.) long.

General description. The heartwood is reddish-brown, darkening on exposure. The texture is even though fairly coarse and the grain is commonly interlocked or wavy. Curly-grained material is sometimes found. The average density is about 0·82 (51 lb./ft.³), seasoned, appreciably heavier than European and American oak.

Seasoning and movement. The timber can be dried without difficulty in thicknesses up to 50 mm. (2 in.), though there is a tendency to warp. Partial air drying before kilning is recommended (FPRL kiln schedule C is suggested). Thick stock is normally air dried, with suitable precautions to prevent checking in the early stages. Movement of seasoned material in use is medium.

Strength and bending properties. Jarrah is 10–20 per cent superior to oak in most strength properties but 40–50 per cent harder. In the Australian classification of structural timbers it is included in Group C. Reasonably straight-grained material is classed as moderately good for steam bending.

Durability and preservative treatment. Jarrah is classed as durable (Class 2) in Australia and as very durable (Class 1) under European conditions. It lasts well in the ground and is resistant to termites and marine borers. It is almost impossible to impregnate but preservative treatment is unnecessary.

Working and finishing properties. The timber is hard but not difficult to work provided tools and cutters are in good condition. In planing quarter-sawn material it is advisable to reduce the cutting angle to 15°. In general it finishes and polishes well and can be glued satisfactorily.

Uses. Because of its strength and durability and the good supplies available, jarrah has been extensively used in Australia and many other parts of the world for railway sleepers and heavy construction, such as railway wagons, bridge and harbour work, piling and mine-shaft guides. The London Underground railways use jarrah sleepers. It is also manufactured into flooring, which has a good appearance and wears well under normal conditions of pedestrian traffic. In Australia it is a standard timber for building and for doors, windows and interior joinery, especially in public buildings, and is also used to some extent for domestic furniture.

Jarrah

Flat cut

Reproduced actual size

Karri

[Eucalyptus diversicolor]

Distribution and supplies. Karri is found in a fairly restricted area of Western Australia. It is an enormous tree, commonly exceeding 60 m. (200 ft.) in height and 2·5 m. (8 ft.) in diameter at the butt, clear of branches to a height of 25–30 m. (say, 80–100 ft.). Large quantities of the timber are produced in a wide range of sizes and continuity of supplies is assured. It is shipped to many parts of the world, mainly on account of the large sizes available. Baulks of heart-free timber up to about 12 m. (40 ft.) in length can be supplied.

General description. Karri closely resembles jarrah in appearance but is generally lighter in colour, straighter in the grain and heavier, average density about 0·90 (56 lb./ft.^{3}), seasoned.

Seasoning and movement. The timber tends to check in seasoning and should be dried slowly, especially material of large dimensions. Stacks of wide boards should be weighted to restrain the tendency to warp and distort. Partial air drying before kilning is advised (using FPRL kiln schedule C). Dimensional movement of seasoned material is large.

Strength and bending properties. Karri is superior to jarrah in all strength properties except shear and resistance to splitting. In the Australian classification of structural timbers it is placed in Group B. Clear material is moderately good for steam bending.

Durability and preservative treatment. It is classed as moderately durable, being inferior to jarrah in this respect. Heartwood is extremely resistant to preservative treatment.

Working and finishing properties. The timber is hard to work in machines and difficult to cut with hand tools. A fairly clean finish can be obtained in most operations. In planing quarter-sawn material it is advisable to reduce the cutting angle to 15°. It finishes and polishes well and can be glued satisfactorily.

Uses. Though inferior to jarrah in its resistance to decay and insect attack, karri has the advantage of superior strength and is obtainable in larger sizes. On these grounds it is sometimes preferred for heavy construction such as in railway wagons, bridges and mine-shaft guides. It is in the same class as jarrah for flooring. Despite its density it can be peeled and is used in Western Australia for the manufacture of plywood.

Karri

Flat cut

  Reproduced actual size

'Mountain Ash' or 'Tasmanian Oak'

[*Eucalyptus regnans*]

The name 'ash' in Australia is generally used for a group of *Eucalyptus* timbers with a superficial resemblance to true ash (*Fraxinus*). In terms of the quantity of timber produced annually 'mountain ash' is the most important species and may be taken as typical of the group. Alternative trade names in Australia are white ash, Tasmanian oak and Australian oak. On the export market timber of the ash group is commonly known as Tasmanian oak, sometimes as Victorian oak or Australian oak.

Distribution and supplies. 'Mountain ash' is found abundantly in Victoria and Tasmania. It is among the tallest trees in the world, often reaching 90 m. (say, 300 ft.) in height, with a long clear bole up to 2 m. (7 ft.) in diameter. The timber is readily available in South-Eastern Australia in a wide range of sizes and is regularly exported. The tree regenerates freely and grows rapidly so future supplies are assured.

General description. The timber varies in colour from a light pinkish-brown shade, suggesting European ash, to light-brown, very like European oak. It is straight grained and fissile with a coarse texture. Flat-sawn material bears a general resemblance to plain European or American oak. The density varies over a wide range, the average being about 0·64 (40 lb./ft.³) after reconditioning.

Seasoning and movement. There is a strong tendency for surface checks to develop in seasoning and collapse is often severe, though the timber responds well to reconditioning treatment. FPRL kiln schedule C is recommended. Dimensional movement in service is large.

Strength and bending properties. In the Australian classification of structural timbers 'mountain ash' is placed in Group C. From the limited data available it appears to be about equal to English oak in hardness and superior in other strength properties. It is classed as moderately good for steam bending.

Durability and preservative treatment. The timber is classed as non-durable in Australia and as moderately durable under European conditions, being inferior to oak in this respect. It is resistant to preservative treatment.

Working and finishing properties. The wood works with moderate ease by hand and machine tools, being slightly less hard to cut than English ash. It finishes cleanly in most operations, takes stain well and can be glued satisfactorily. Treatment with ammonia fumes produces a pale walnut colour.

Uses. In Australia 'mountain ash' is used for a wide range of purposes including flooring, weather-boarding, house framing, interior joinery, furniture, boxes and crates, cooperage, handles for shovels, brooms, rakes, etc., oars, ship and boat building, plywood, matches, wood wool, and paper pulp. In Britain it is probably best known as a flooring timber.

Other species of interest. *Timber exported under the name of Tasmanian oak or Victorian oak comprises three principal species: alpine ash (*E. delegatensis *or* E. gigantea*), messmate stringybark (*E. obliqua*) and mountain ash (described above).*

'Mountain Ash' or 'Tasmanian Oak'
Flat cut

  Reproduced actual size

Mulga

[Acacia aneura]

Distribution and supplies. Mulga is a small tree, 4·5–6·0 m. (15–20 ft.) high, found mainly in the extremely dry interior of South Australia. The irregular bole is rarely more than about 4·5 m. (15 ft.) long and 250 mm. (10 in.) in diameter.

General description. The wood is highly distinctive in appearance, dark-brown with contrasting golden-yellow markings, an extremely fine, even texture and straight grain. It is one of the hardest and heaviest woods known; in the seasoned condition it has a density of about 1·20 (75 lb./ft.^{3}).

Technical properties and uses. Mulga turns well, finishing to a glassy surface, and takes a high polish. It is in demand for making the ornamental woodware that is familiar in Australian homes and has been exported to many other countries.
A special technique has been developed to dry the wood without checking and to keep the bark firmly adhering to the wood. Mulga is used by the aborigines for making their boomerangs, spear-points and other weapons. It makes strong, durable fence posts and bullock yokes and provides valuable fuel, in the natural condition and as charcoal.

130

Mulga
Flat cut

 Reproduced actual size

'Queensland Maple'

[*Flindersia brayleyana* and *F. pimenteliana*]

'Queensland maple' is the standard name for this timber in Australia and on the export market. It should be noted, however, that it is not related to the true maple (*Acer*) of the northern hemisphere. It is also known as silkwood and maple silkwood.

Distribution and supplies. The tree is confined to Queensland where it grows to a height of about 30 m. (100 ft.) and a diameter of 1·2 m. (4 ft.), though the average diameter of logs is nearer 0·75 m. (2 ft. 6 in.). In Australia the timber is available in a wide range of board and joinery sizes and as veneers, plywood, laminated panels and flush doors. The export trade is mainly in decorative veneers.

General description. A highly decorative timber with similarities to mahogany and walnut, light pinkish-brown darkening to a medium-brown shade with a silky lustre. The grain is often interlocked and may also be wavy or curly, giving rise to a wide range of figure. The average density is 0·55 (34 lb./ft.^{3}), seasoned, which is about the same as mahogany.

Seasoning. The timber can be dried without difficulty in thicknesses up to 75 mm. (3 in.) though there is a tendency to collapse and warp, particularly in the denser material. FPRL kiln schedule C is suggested.

Strength and bending properties. Strong for its weight, similar to oak in most respects, but rated poor for steam bending.

Durability. Non-durable under conditions favouring decay.

Working and finishing properties. The timber works fairly readily in most hand and machine operations. Quartered stock with interlocked grain has a tendency to pick up in planing but this is reduced if a cutting angle of 20° is used. A good finish is generally obtained in other operations and polishing gives excellent results.

Uses. 'Queensland maple' is the premier cabinet timber of Australia where it is widely used also for decorative panelling, joinery and interior fittings, both in the solid and as veneer. The best veneers are obtained from stumps, butt logs and crotches. The timber is excellent for railway carriage building, boat building and rifle stocks.

'Queensland Maple'

Butt

 Reproduced two-thirds actual size

133

'Queensland Walnut'

[*Endiandra palmerstonii*]

'Queensland walnut' is so called from its resemblance to true walnut. It is also known as walnut bean in Australia and as oriental wood in USA.

Distribution and supplies. This species is confined to Northern Queensland where it is a common tree with a well-shaped bole up to 1·8 m. (6 ft.) in diameter, clear of branches to a height of 25 m. (80 ft.) or more. The timber is well known in Britain and USA as an alternative to true walnut. Supplies are mainly in the form of veneer but sawn material is obtainable also.

General description. This highly decorative wood resembles European rather than American walnut, being chocolate-brown with pinkish, grey-green or nearly black streaks which are typically more regular than in true walnut. The grain is more or less interlocked and frequently wavy, giving rise to a broken stripe figure on quarter-cut material. The texture is fairly fine and even. When freshly cut the wood has a peculiar, unpleasant odour which disappears in time. It is slightly heavier than European walnut, average density about 0·67 (42 lb./ft.^{3}), seasoned.

Seasoning and movement. The timber dries fairly rapidly and well in small dimensions, though there is a tendency to warp. End-coating is advised to prevent splitting. FPRL kiln schedule E is suggested.

Strength and bending properties. Results of limited tests indicate that 'Queensland walnut' is considerably stronger than European walnut. It is classed as moderately good for steam bending.

Durability and preservative treatment. Non-durable. No information is available on preservative treatment.

Working and finishing properties. A disadvantage is the high silica content which has the effect of rapidly dulling the cutting edges of tools. Special saws, tipped with tungsten carbide or similar material, are advised. In planing, the best-quality high-speed steel cutters are required and a cutting angle of 20° should be used to obtain a good finish.

Uses. 'Queensland walnut' is used, mainly in the form of veneer, for furniture and cabinet work, panelling and interior joinery such as shop fittings. As a flooring timber it is classed as moderately resistant to wear.

Other species of interest. *Some other Australian timbers known as walnut are* Endiandra virens *(New South Wales walnut),* E. discolor *(rose walnut),* E. sieberi *(pink walnut),* Beilschmiedia bancroftii *(yellow walnut) and* B. obtusifolia *(blush walnut).*

'Queensland Walnut'

Quarter cut

Reproduced actual size

Silky Oak

[Cardwellia sublimis]

Distribution and supplies. *Cardwellia sublimis* (northern silky oak) is the most important of a number of closely allied Australian timbers collectively known as silky oak. It is a common tree in the tropical coastal forests of Northern Queensland, growing to a height of 30 m. (100 ft.) or more and a diameter of 1·25 m. (4 ft.). In Australia the timber is available in a range of sizes, up to 450 mm. (18 in.) wide, and as veneer and plywood. It is exported mainly as decorative veneer or as flitches for the manufacture of veneer.

General description. Although botanically unrelated to true oak, silky oak has some resemblance to oak in appearance, due to the broad rays which give the wood a conspicuous, highly characteristic silver-grain figure when cut on the quarter. The heartwood is pinkish-brown or reddish-brown, darkening on exposure, with a natural silky lustre. It is moderately coarse textured, generally straight grained and moderately light in weight, average density about 0·53 (33 lb./ft.³), seasoned, which is much lighter than true oak.

Seasoning. Australian experience indicates there is little risk of degrade in kiln seasoning provided the timber is dried slowly. FPRL kiln schedule E would appear to be suitable.

Strength and bending properties. It is described as a light, soft timber but firm, strong and tough for its weight and is reputed to be very good for steam bending.

Durability. Silky oak does not compare with true oak in its lasting qualities. The heartwood is classed as moderately durable. The sapwood is particularly susceptible to attack by powder-post beetles.

Working and finishing properties. The wood works easily by hand or machine tools with little dulling effect on cutting edges. Planed surfaces tend to be a little rough; sharp cutters and a cutting angle of 20° are advisable to obtain a good finish. Good results are obtained with gluing, staining and polishing. Nailing and screwing present no difficulties. Silky oak is reported to peel and slice well, giving a flexible veneer.

Uses. Because of its good working and finishing properties and attractive appearance, silky oak is popular in Australia for furniture, cabinet work, panelling and interior joinery. It is also used for turned goods such as chair legs, brush backs and ornamental work, for general building purposes, for bentwork in railway coaches and for plywood. In Britain it is seen mainly as decorative veneer.

Other species of interest. *Another species of silky oak,* Grevillea robusta, *a native of Eastern Australia, has been planted extensively as a shade tree on coffee and tea plantations in Africa, India, Ceylon and other parts of the world. The timber resembles the Australian silky oak described above but is generally inferior in quality, being the product of relatively small trees with short stems and heavy branching.*

Silky Oak

Quarter cut

Reproduced actual size

Tallowwood

[Eucalyptus microcorys]

Distribution and supplies. Tallowwood is a common tree in the coastal forests of New South Wales and Queensland, growing to a height of 45 m. (150 ft.) and a diameter of 1 m. or more (say, 4 ft.). The timber is available locally in fairly large quantities, in structural sizes and as boards. This species is grown successfully in plantations in other parts of the world.

General description. As the name implies, tallowwood is of a waxy nature. It is yellowish-brown with a moderately coarse, even texture and a typically interlocked grain which, combined with the natural lustre of the wood, gives it an attractive appearance. It is hard and heavy, average density about 0·98 (61 lb./ft.³), seasoned.

Seasoning and movement. The timber is liable to split and check in drying, particularly when flat-sawn. One-inch stock can be kiln dried from the green condition but thicker material should be given a preliminary period of air seasoning. FPRL kiln schedule C is suggested. Dimensional movement in service is medium.

Strength and bending properties. In the Australian strength classification tallowwood is one of the less heavy timbers in Group A. In most respects it is about twice as strong as oak but its resistance to splitting is relatively poor. It is classed as moderately good for steam bending.

Durability and preservative treatment. This timber is highly resistant to fungal decay and attack by insects, including termites. It is practically impermeable to liquids.

Working and finishing properties. Considering its density the wood is only moderately difficult to work. In planing, if the cutting angle is reduced to 20° it finishes to a smooth greasy surface. For a satisfactory glue joint, a wash with a 10 per cent solution of caustic soda is recommended.

Uses. In Australia tallowwood is used for a wide range of purposes where strength and durability are important, including posts and poles, railway sleepers, railway wagons, bridge timbers and building work. As flooring it wears well and presents a good appearance and is considered the best Australian timber for dance floors and skating rinks. In industrial buildings it is suitable for light-duty flooring but it tends to splinter or roughen under heavy traffic conditions.

Tallowwood

Flat cut

Reproduced actual size

Turpentine

[Syncarpia glomulifera, formerly *S. laurifolia]*

The common name turpentine is due to the oleo-resin in the inner bark. The alternative name lustre is reserved for specially prepared timber, as used for flooring.

Distribution and supplies: The tree is found in the coastal forests of New South Wales and Queensland; it grows to a height of 40 m. (130 ft.) or more, with a slim, clear bole 1 m. (3 ft. 3 in.) or more in diameter. The timber is in good supply, sawn, hewn and in log form.

General description. The heartwood is red or reddish-brown with a natural lustre, a fine to medium texture and interlocked or wavy grain. Density is variable, commonly of the order of 0·95 (59 lb./ft.³), seasoned.

Seasoning. Flat-sawn material is likely to develop surface checks in drying; quarter-sawn stock up to 25 mm. (1 in.) thick can be dried without serious degrade, except that collapse is liable to occur, necessitating a final reconditioning treatment. Air drying to a moisture content of 30 per cent or less is recommended as a preliminary to kiln seasoning.

Strength and bending properties. In the Australian classification of structural timbers, turpentine is placed in Group B. It is described as being satisfactory for steam bending.

Durability. Turpentine is resistant to fungal decay and insect attack, including termites, and is classed as very durable. It is outstanding in its resistance to marine borers.

Working and finishing properties. The timber is inclined to dull saw teeth and planer knives but, considering its density, is fairly easy to work, turns well and takes a good finish.

Uses. Turpentine is one of the best Australian timbers for wharf piles and other marine work, including shipbuilding and underwater planking and sheeting. It is also in demand for fence posts, railway sleepers, railway wagons and other heavy construction. When used for wharf decking and flooring it wears exceptionally well without splintering.

Other species of interest. *Satinay (S. hillii), of Fraser Island off the coast of Queensland, resembles turpentine in general character but takes a better finish and has a more attractive appearance. It is used for high-class furniture and panelling as well as flooring and constructional work.*

Turpentine

Flat cut

Reproduced actual size

Wandoo

[Eucalyptus redunca var. elata]

Distribution and supplies. An important timber tree of Western Australia, attaining a height of 37 m. (120 ft.) with a clear bole of 9–12 m. (30–40 ft.) and a diameter of about 1·2 m. (4 ft.). The timber is in good supply, in round, hewn and sawn form.

General description. Essentially a heavy structural timber, light reddish-brown, sometimes with a yellowish tint. Close textured, grain usually wavy or interlocked. One of the heaviest and most durable of Australian timbers, similar to ironbark in this respect, average density about 1·10 (69 lb./ft.^{3}), seasoned.

Seasoning. A slow-drying timber with a tendency to develop surface checks and end splits. Air seasoning to a moisture content of 30 per cent is recommended before final kiln drying treatment.

Strength properties. In the Australian classification of structural timbers, wandoo is placed in Group A with ironbark, spotted gum and tallowwood. It is described as very hard, exceedingly strong and stiff and very tough.

Durability and preservative treatment. Wandoo is highly resistant to fungal decay and insect attack, including termites, and is classed as very durable. It is not the kind of timber that requires preservative treatment.

Working and finishing properties. The timber is difficult to work with hand tools, but it machines satisfactorily.

Uses. Wandoo is suitable for purposes where strength and durability are important. It is used in Australia for railway sleepers, bridge and wharf construction, the underframes of railway wagons, heavy-duty flooring and wheelwrights' work. One of its main uses is as a source of tannin for the leather industry.

Wandoo

Flat cut

Reproduced actual size

143

Australian Timbers
SOFTWOODS

Cypress Pine

[principally *Callitris glauca*]

Cypress pine is the Australian standard name for the timber of species of *Callitris*, a group of conifers confined to Australia. Except where otherwise stated the following description refers to white cypress pine or Murray pine (*C. glauca*), the principal source of commercial timber.

Distribution and supplies. White cypress pine is widely distributed in the dry interior of Australia. Generally the trees are relatively small but may reach a height of 24–30 m. (80–100 ft.) and a diameter of about 0·5 m. (18–20 in.). In the aggregate the supply of timber is considerable. Other species of *Callitris* are too small or too rare to be of much economic importance but their timber is used to some extent locally.

General description. The yellowish-brown heartwood is marked with darker streaks to give a decorative appearance. The grain is generally straight though small firm knots are common. The wood has an aromatic camphor-like odour. For a softwood it is fairly hard and heavy, average density 0·67 (42 lb./ft.^{3}) in the seasoned condition

Seasoning. Timber from logs of fair, average quality can be dried without difficulty though some checking and distortion occurs in the neighbourhood of knots.

Strength properties. In the Australian classification of structural timbers white cypress pine is included in Group D, with hoop pine. Though strong enough for ordinary constructional work it is exceptionally brittle.

Durability. This is the only Australian softwood to be classed as very durable. Its resistance to fungal decay and attack by insects, including termites, is ascribed to the presence of resinous extractives which incidentally make the timber extremely inflammable.

Working and finishing properties. For a softwood cypress pine is fairly hard to work with hand tools. It machines well to a smooth finish and takes a high polish. The finished surface is somewhat greasy to the touch.

Uses. This timber is largely used for house building in termite-infested areas, notably the inland districts of Queensland and New South Wales. On account of its attractive appearance and good wearing qualities it makes a good parquet floor. Figured material is selected for furniture and interior fittings. Round poles and posts are extensively used for fencing, etc.

Other species of interest. *King William pine (Athrotaxis selaginoides) of Tasmania is closely allied to California redwood and the timber is similar in character, being reddish in colour, light in weight and durable. The limited supplies are used mainly for house joinery such as doors and window frames.*

Celery-top pine (Phyllocladus asplenifolius), also of Tasmania, is comparatively heavy for a softwood and is resistant to decay. A useful timber, available only in small quantities.

Queensland kauri is briefly described under the heading of New Zealand kauri. Huon pine is referred to under New Zealand rimu.

146

Cypress Pine

Flat cut

Reproduced actual size

Hoop Pine

[*Araucaria cunninghamii*]

Hoop pine is the standard Australian name for the timber of *Araucaria cunninghamii,* also known as colonial pine, Dorrigo pine, Richmond River pine and Queensland pine. The last name is also applied to *A. bidwillii* (see below).

Distribution and supplies. This important conifer occurs naturally in the coastal forests of Queensland and New South Wales. Under favourable conditions it grows to a height of 30–45 m. (say, 100–150 ft.), with a cylindrical bole clear of branches to a height of 18 m. (60 ft.), up to 1 m. (3 ft. 3 in.) or so in diameter. The better stands have been heavily depleted and plantations have been established on a fairly large scale to maintain supplies. The tree is also found in New Guinea.

General description. The timber resembles Parana pine and kauri in general character, being light yellowish-brown, rarely with a pinkish tinge, with inconspicuous growth rings and consequently a fine, even texture. The grain is typically straight. Darker-coloured bands of compression wood are liable to occur and small pin knots are characteristic, though clear timber can be obtained by selection. Average density is about 0·55 (34 lb./ft.^{3}), seasoned.

Seasoning. Clear timber dries quickly and well; material up to 50 mm. (2 in.) thick can be kiln dried from the green condition without degrade but distortion can be expected if compression wood is present. Sapwood is liable to be affected by blue stain.

Strength and bending properties. In the Australian classification of structural timbers hoop pine falls in Group D. It is approximately equivalent to Douglas fir but its impact strength is low with a brittle fracture. It is not good for steam bending.

Durability and preservative treatment. A non-durable timber, i.e. not suitable for use out of doors unless it has been painted or treated with a preservative.

Working and finishing properties. The wood can be worked easily by hand and machine tools, is easy to nail and takes a clean, smooth finish. It gives good results with glue and the usual finishing treatments.

Uses. Hoop pine is largely used in Australia for flooring, interior joinery, boxes and packing cases. It is particularly suitable for the manufacture of plywood and veneer. Other uses include agricultural implements, broom handles, matches and match boxes.

Other species of interest. *Bunya pine (A. bidwillii) is very similar to hoop pine. It can sometimes be distinguished by its pinkish colour and lighter weight (average density 0·45, i.e. 28 lb./ft.^{3}, seasoned) and has the advantage of being relatively free from compression wood. The tree has a limited range of distribution in South-Eastern Queensland where the timber is commonly sold in mixture with hoop pine under the name of Queensland pine.*

Klinki pine (A. klinkii) is found at high altitudes in New Guinea in association with hoop pine. The tree grows to a large size with a long, clear bole. The timber is in good supply and of excellent quality. It has been shipped to Australia and USA in the form of logs, lumber, veneer and plywood. It resembles hoop pine in general character and is suitable for the same purposes though it is appreciably lighter in weight, average density 0·45 (28 lb./ft.^{3}), seasoned. The heartwood has a purplish tint and there is sometimes an attractive birdseye figure.

Two Australian species of Podocarpus, P. amara and P. elata, commonly known as black pine and brown pine respectively, are frequently mixed with hoop pine, bunya pine or kauri and sold as such.

Hoop Pine

Flat cut

Reproduced actual size

149

New Zealand Timbers
HARDWOODS

Beech, Silver

[Nothofagus menziesii]

Distribution and supplies. Silver beech or Southland beech is the principal New Zealand species of *Nothofagus,* the beech of the Southern Hemisphere. It is widely distributed in both North and South Islands as a medium-sized to tall tree with a merchantable bole usually 9–12 m. (30–45 ft.) in length, 0·6–1·2 m. (2–4 ft.) in diameter. An important source of general-utility and special-purpose hardwood for local use and one of the few indigenous timbers expected to continue in good supply.

General description. A light- to medium-density hardwood of plain appearance, resembling Northern Hemisphere beech and birch but lacking the characteristic large rays of true beech. The heartwood is a lustrous, uniform pinkish-brown with a fine, even texture and usually a straight grain. Density varies with locality of growth, sufficiently to justify distinguishing timber from Southland, the preferred type (averaging about 0·55 (34 lb./ft.³)), Nelson (slightly denser) and North Island (0·74 (46 lb./ft.³)).

Seasoning. The timber dries fairly readily, flat-sawn material more quickly than quarter-sawn. Distortion is comparatively slight but there is some tendency for end-splitting to develop. FPRL kiln schedule E is recommended.

Strength and bending properties. The Southland timber in the seasoned condition is above normal strength for its weight in almost all properties. It is weaker than European beech except in resistance to shock. Limited tests indicate that it is good for steam bending.

Durability and preservative treatment. The heartwood should probably be classed as non-durable. It is extremely resistant to pressure treatment but good penetration is obtained using the diffusion process. The sapwood is seldom attacked by wood-boring insects.

Working and finishing properties. Silver beech saws and machines easily and takes a good finish. The Southland timber has less dulling effect than European beech. It has reasonably good nailing and screwing properties, takes a satisfactory finish with stain or polish and takes paint well without special treatment.

Uses. High-grade Southland silver beech is a versatile timber, suitable for a wide range of uses, including high-class furniture, turnery, boat building, brush backs, flooring and interior finish. Lower grades are used for building construction and boxes.

Other species of interest. *Red beech (N. fusca) is harder and denser than Southland silver beech, averaging about 0·72 (45 lb./ft.³), seasoned, and correspondingly stronger and more durable. It is difficult to season but has good working and finishing properties. Principal uses are bridges, wharf decking, gates and fencing, railway sleepers, flooring and boat building.*

Hard beech (N. truncata) is harder, stronger, denser and more durable than red beech, average density about 0·77 (48 lb./ft.³), seasoned, used mainly for heavy constructional work such as mine timbers, fence posts, bridge timbers and industrial flooring.

Beech, Silver

Quarter cut

 Reproduced actual size

New Zealand Timbers
SOFTWOODS

Kahikatea or New Zealand White Pine

[Podocarpus dacrydioides]

Distribution and supplies. Kahikatea occurs throughout New Zealand. The merchantable bole is normally 15–18 m. (50–60 ft.) long, of excellent cylindrical form above the butt section, the diameter sometimes nearly 1·8 m. (6 ft.), usually 0·5–1·25 m. (say, 1·5–4 ft.). The limited supplies of timber are of importance for its special uses and the clear, wide boards available.

General description. A light, soft timber, consisting mainly of white sapwood with a small yellow, resinous heartwood. There is no distinct figure. The texture is fine and even, growth rings being poorly defined. The grain is straight. Average density is about 0·45 (28 lb./ft.^{3}), seasoned. The wood is odourless and tasteless.

Seasoning and movement. Sawn timber dries evenly and quickly. Anti-sapstain treatment is advisable. Heartwood is stable, sapwood unstable.

Strength properties. Kahikatea is one of the weaker New Zealand timbers. However, it has a reputation for withstanding rough usage.

Durability and preservative treatment. The perishable sapwood is liable to sapstain and woodworm; it is easily treated by pressure methods. The heartwood is classed as non-durable but lasts well out of contact with the ground.

Working and finishing properties. Easy to work by hand or machine tools. Painting qualities of both sapwood and heartwood are excellent.

Uses. Kahikatea is unique among New Zealand timbers for combining a clean white appearance (sapwood), freedom from taint, ability to withstand rough usage and good working properties, which make it specially suitable for butter boxes, cheese crates and dairy equipment. The general adoption of fibreboard containers for New Zealand butter has released supplies of the timber for general purposes such as weatherboarding, joinery, flooring and veneers.

Kahikatea or New Zealand White Pine
Flat cut

Reproduced actual size

Kauri, New Zealand

[Agathis australis]

Distribution and supplies. Kauri is the largest and most renowned of all New Zealand timber trees. It attains a height of 25–40 m. (80–130 ft.) or more with a massive columnar trunk, normally 9–18 m. (30–60 ft.) long and 1–2 m. (say, 3–7 ft.) in diameter. The timber has a world-wide reputation but resources are now seriously depleted and can do no more than supply a few special-purpose requirements. There are prospects of increased supplies of small-dimension material from regenerating forests and from plantations.

General description. Unlike the majority of commercial softwoods kauri has ill-defined growth rings with no clear distinction between spring wood and summer wood. The wood is straight grained with a fine, even, silky texture and a lustrous surface. The heartwood is normally a light biscuit colour but where there is a heavy infiltration of resin it may be yellowish-brown or reddish-brown. It is normally of plain appearance with a distinctive speckle due to the resinous rays. Irregularities of the grain sometimes produce an attractive mottle. The average density of seasoned timber is about 0·58 (36 lb./ft.³).

Seasoning and movement. The timber dries well but fairly slowly with little degrade and is dimensionally stable in service. FPRL kiln schedule J is suggested.

Strength properties. New Zealand kauri is practically equal to pitch pine in strength except that in the seasoned condition it is about 25 per cent weaker in longitudinal compression.

Durability and preservative treatment. In a temperate climate the heartwood is rated moderately durable in contact with the ground. It is very durable under hot, wet conditions, as in vats for certain industrial processes. It is not readily permeable to liquids and is resistant to preservative treatment.

Working and finishing properties. The timber works easily and finishes with a clean, smooth surface. It has good nailing and screwing properties, takes stain, paint and polish well and can be glued satisfactorily.

Uses. Because of its outstanding technical qualities and the large sizes of clear material available, New Zealand kauri was formerly one of the principal timbers used in Britain and elsewhere for vats and tanks and in boat building but is now difficult to obtain outside the country of origin.

Other species of interest. *Queensland kauri, derived from* A. robusta, A. palmerstonii *and* A. microstachya, *has a general resemblance to the more valuable New Zealand species but is appreciably lighter in weight and correspondingly inferior in strength. The limited supplies are absorbed in Australia for joinery and cabinet work, engineers' patterns, butter boxes and plywood. Fijian kauri (*A. vitiensis*) has been tried in Britain for vats as an alternative to the New Zealand timber and found to be unsuitable because of its permeability. One or more other species are found in the Malay Peninsula, Indonesia, Borneo, the Philippines and the Pacific Islands. Malayan kauri is sufficiently important to be included in the Malayan Grading Rules for sawn timber. It more closely resembles Queensland kauri than the heavier New Zealand timber. The same or a closely allied species in Sabah is reported to be of almost no commercial interest because of its inaccessibility in mountainous country, though supplies may become available as logging operations are extended. The timber is not durable under tropical conditions. It peels well and makes excellent plywood.*

158

Kauri, New Zealand

Quarter cut

Reproduced actual size

Matai or New Zealand Black Pine

[Podocarpus spicatus]

Distribution and supplies. Widely distributed in New Zealand. The timber is in better supply than that of other indigenous species of *Podocarpus*. The merchantable bole rarely exceeds 12 m. (40 ft.) in length and 1 m. (3 ft. 3 in.) in diameter.

General description. Matai is known for its high yield of clear heartwood, yellowish-brown to orange-brown. The white sapwood is comparatively narrow. The texture is fine and even, the grain straight. Rather hard and heavy for a softwood, average density about 0·61 (38 lb./ft.^{3}), seasoned.

Seasoning and movement. The timber dries very well with little shrinkage. Heartwood is exceptionally stable, sapwood slightly less so.

Strength and bending properties. Strength properties of matai are such as to commend it for use as posts and columns rather than beams and joists. Large sections are liable to brittle fracture across the grain. Compared with rimu, which is taken as the standard indigenous New Zealand softwood, it is some 12 per cent stronger in compression and about equal in bending strength. Steam bending qualities are moderately good.

Durability and preservative treatment. Heartwood is moderately durable in contact with the ground, moderately resistant to preservative treatment. Sapwood is non-durable and subject to woodworm attack but not particularly susceptible to sapstain.

Working and finishing properties. Heartwood machines excellently and peels well. When dry it should be pre-bored for nailing to prevent splitting. Well-seasoned wood, unless very resinous, has good painting qualities.

Uses. For building work the better grades are generally reserved for strip flooring, weatherboarding and exterior joinery, especially sills. Lower grades are used for framing and rough carpentry.

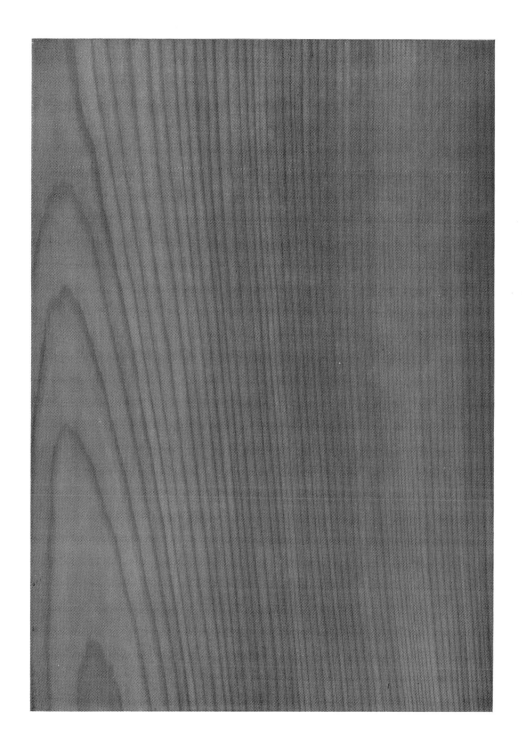

Matai or New Zealand Black Pine

Flat cut

Reproduced actual size

Miro

[Podocarpus ferrugineus]

Distribution and supplies. Miro is found in indigenous forest throughout New Zealand wherever rimu occurs. A medium-sized tree with a merchantable bole usually less than 12 m. (40 ft.) in length and 1 m. (3 ft. 3 in.) in diameter. The timber is often sold as rimu.

General description. There is a general resemblance to rimu though miro has a less attractive appearance. A smudgy dark pigment figure overlies the light-brown heartwood which is greyish as compared with the reddish shade of rimu. Like rimu, miro has an intermediate zone between heartwood and sapwood. The grain is moderately straight, the texture fine and even. Average density is about 0·58 (36 lb./ft.^{3}), seasoned.

Seasoning and movement. The timber dries readily with a slightly greater tendency to warp than rimu. Heartwood is dimensionally stable, sapwood unstable.

Strength and bending properties. Miro is one of the stronger native New Zealand softwoods, being stronger and harder than rimu and only slightly inferior to kauri. It is good for steam bending.

Durability and preservative treatment. The heartwood is moderately durable, similar to rimu in this respect, and resistant to preservative treatment. The sapwood is more susceptible to *Anobium* attack and more resistant to treatment than rimu.

Working and finishing properties. Miro has excellent machining and finishing properties. It is slightly more difficult than rimu to work with hand tools and to nail without splitting.

Uses. Practically the entire output of miro is consumed by the New Zealand building industry where it is used in the same way as rimu, notably for flooring, weatherboarding and interior finish. Lower grades are used for framing and rough carpentry.

Miro

Flat cut

Reproduced actual size

Pine, Radiata or Monterey

[Pinus radiata]

Distribution and supplies. The natural distribution is restricted to a narrow coastal strip of Southern California. Here the tree is of little interest as a source of timber but in other parts of the world, especially in the Southern Hemisphere (Australia, New Zealand, South Africa and Chile) and in Spain, it has assumed great importance as an exotic, remarkable for its rapid growth and high yield of lumber and wood pulp. It is particularly associated with New Zealand where it provides about half the annual cut of timber. New Zealand and Chile have a large exportable surplus. Under favourable conditions plantation-grown trees reach a height of 28–34 m. (91–110 ft.) and a diameter at breast height of 280–500 mm. (11–20 in.) in 20 years.

General description. The creamy-white sapwood is exceptionally wide, distinct from the pinkish-brown heartwood which occupies only about 15–20 per cent of the total volume. Growth rings show comparatively little contrast between spring wood and summer wood; consequently the texture is moderately fine and even. The grain is typically straight except in the neighbourhood of knots and at the heart centre. There is a slightly resinous odour. The core of low-density juvenile wood surrounding the large pith is commonly 100–125 mm. (4–5 in.) in diameter, corresponding to four years of rapid growth; this wood has inferior technical properties. Outside the central core the density increases. The average density of timber grown in New Zealand is about 0·48 (30 lb./ft.^{3}), seasoned. In Australia, South Africa and Chile the figure is slightly higher.

Seasoning and movement. Seasoning presents no difficulty. The sawn timber dries rapidly with little degrade; for example, under good conditions 25 mm. (1 in.) stock can be air dried in six weeks. FPRL kiln schedule K is suggested. The heartwood is classed as stable, the sapwood not stable (medium movement).

Strength and bending properties. Strength varies considerably but is generally high for the density. On average the timber is softer than Baltic redwood, harder than ponderosa pine. Steam bending qualities are poor.

Durability and preservative treatment. The sapwood, which provides the bulk of the commercial timber, is subject to attack by sapstain fungi and wood-boring insects and is perishable under conditions favourable to decay. The heartwood is resistant to wood borers and is durable above ground. The sapwood is readily treated by diffusion, steeping or pressure methods. The heartwood is resistant or moderately resistant to impregnation.

Working and finishing properties. Sawing and machining qualities are complicated only by the presence of knots. Clean timber machines well to a smooth, clean finish provided that cutters with sharp, thin edges are used. It takes nails fairly well and gives good results with glue and paint but not with stain.

Uses. The principal uses for the timber are packing cases, light and heavy construction and shuttering. In spite of the wide rings, the even texture of the wood makes the higher grades suitable for furniture and joinery. Selected logs are peeled for veneer and plywood. The wood is also largely used for pulp and paper, fibreboard and particle board.

Pine, Radiata or Monterey

Quarter cut

Reproduced actual size

Rimu

[Dacrydium cupressinum]

Distribution and supplies. Rimu is widely distributed throughout New Zealand and is frequently a dominant species of the indigenous forests, where it is the most important softwood. A tall tree with a merchantable bole normally in the range 9–21 m. (30–70 ft.), up to 2 m. (6 ft. 6 in.) in diameter. The timber is in good supply in a wide range of sizes, though the annual cut is declining.

General description. The attractively figured heartwood (yellow-brown to reddish-brown with irregular streaks) comprises up to 33 per cent of the volume of large logs. There is a fairly well-defined, evenly coloured, light-brown intermediate zone between the heartwood and the paler sapwood. Growth rings are usually narrow and not very sharply defined. The texture is fine and even, the grain straight. The average density of seasoned timber is about 0·60 (37 lb./ft.^{3}).

Seasoning and movement. The timber dries readily without serious degrade though the difference in the drying rates of heartwood and sapwood is liable to cause distortion. Heartwood is dimensionally stable, sapwood unstable.

Strength and bending properties. Rimu possesses fairly good strength properties, little inferior to those of Douglas fir except in compression along the grain. It is good for steam bending.

Durability and preservative treatment. The heartwood is not durable in the ground and is resistant to preservative treatment. The sapwood is moderately easy to treat by pressure and diffusion methods.

Working and finishing properties. Rimu heartwood is fairly hard to work but machines excellently. Because the dry wood cannot be nailed without pre-boring it is customary to use it unseasoned for framing. Sapwood works easily with hand or machine tools. Both sapwood and heartwood give good results with painting and natural finishes and can be glued satisfactorily.

Uses. Being generally available in New Zealand in a wide range of sizes and usually free of defects, rimu is the most popular timber for building construction, weatherboarding, interior and exterior joinery, furniture and many other purposes. Clear heartwood makes a decorative, hard, even-wearing floor. Wood from the outer zones is made into crates and boxes, including butter boxes. Rimu is the principal New Zealand species used for plywood.

Other species of interest. *Closely allied to rimu is New Zealand silver pine, D. colensoi, a comparatively small tree of local importance as a source of round timber for use as poles and posts. The heartwood is exceptionally durable. Preservative treatment is unnecessary as the sapwood is very narrow.*

Huon pine is the standard trade name in Australia for the timber of D. franklinii, which is confined to Tasmania. The timber is noted for its durability and good working properties and is highly valued for boat building, joinery and engineers' patterns.

In Sabah and Sarawak the local species of Dacrydium are known as sempilor. The timber was formerly exported but accessible supplies are now almost exhausted.

Rimu

Flat cut

Quarter cut

Reproduced actual size

Totara

[Podocarpus totara and *P. hallii]*

Distribution and supplies. Totara is widely distributed in New Zealand in much the same places as matai. As with other indigenous softwoods supplies are diminishing.

General description. The plain, pinkish-brown heartwood comprises the bulk of this valuable timber, which is characterised by a fine, even texture and straight grain. Average density is about 0·48 (30 lb./ft.³), seasoned.

Seasoning and movement. Sawn timber in thicknesses up to 25 mm. (1 in.) air-seasons readily and without serious degrade. Thick stock (50 mm. (2 in.) and up) dries slowly and unevenly. Kiln drying is not recommended but if necessary FPRL schedule J can be used. Well-seasoned heartwood is stable in use.

Strength properties. When dry totara is inclined to be brittle and is more suitable as a post than a beam. Compared with Baltic redwood it is some 25 per cent inferior in bending strength and stiffness and almost 15 per cent lower in compressive strength.

Durability and preservative treatment. Totara heartwood is well known for its lasting qualities and is classed as durable. It is resistant to impregnation but does not require preservative treatment. The sapwood is moderately resistant to treatment.

Working and finishing properties. The timber works well in all hand and machine operations and takes a good clean finish. It holds screws and nails well. Special priming paints are recommended for the resinous heartwood.

Uses. Because of its excellent working properties, stability and durability, high-grade totara is traditionally preferred for exterior joinery, such as doors and windows, and for tanks, vats and boat sheathing. It is readily split for fence posts, shingles and the like. Lower grades are largely used for fencing.

168

Totara
Flat cut

 Reproduced actual size

169

Literature References

General

A Handbook of Hardwoods (Forest Products Research Laboratory, HM Stationery Office, London, 1956)

A Handbook of Softwoods (FPRL, HMSO, 1960)

Nomenclature of Commercial Timbers, including Sources of Supply. British Standards 881 and 589 (British Standards Institution, London, 1955)

Nomenclature Générale des Bois Tropicaux (Association Technique Internationale des Bois Tropicaux, Nogent-sur-Marne, 1965)

Tropical Timber. Statistics on Production and Trade. (Organisation for Economic Cooperation and Development, Paris, 1967)

Commercial Timbers of India. By R. S. Pearson and H. P. Brown (Government of India Central Publication Branch, Calcutta, 1932)

Indian Woods, their Identification, Properties and Uses. By various authors (Forest Research Institute, Dehra Dun. Vol. 1, 1958, Vol. 2, 1963. To be completed in six volumes)

A Note on the Timber Resources of Pakistan. By S. M. Ishaq (Ministry of Food and Agriculture, Karachi, 1952)

A Handbook of the Forest Products of Burma. By A. Rodger (Bombay, 1943)

Manual of Malayan Timbers. By H. E. Desch (Malayan Forest Records No. 15, Kuala Lumpur, 1941)

Properties and Uses of Commercially Important Japanese Woods. By H. D. Bruce, R. A. Cockrell and L. J. Cummings (General H.Q., Supreme Commander for the Allied Powers, Natural Resources Section, Report No. 147, Tokyo, 1951)

The 'Philippine Mahogany' and Other Dipterocarp Woods. By F. Tamesis and L. Aguilar (Popular Bulletin No. 44, Department of Agriculture and Natural Resources, Manila, 1953)

Timbers of Sabah. By P. F. Burgess (Sabah Forest Record No. 6, Sandakan, 1966)

Forest Trees of Sarawak and Brunei. By F. G. Browne (Kuching, 1955)

Common Sarawak Trees. By B. E. Smythies (Kuching, 1965)

The Commercial Timbers of Australia, their Properties and Uses. By I. H. Boas (Melbourne, 1947)

The Timbers and Forest Products of Queensland. By E. H. F. Swain (Brisbane, 1928)

Forest Trees and Timbers of New Zealand. By H. V. Hinds and J. S. Reid (New Zealand Forest Service bulletin No. 12, Wellington, 1957)

Seasoning and Movement

Timber Seasoning (Timber Research and Development Association, 1962)

Kiln Operator's Handbook. A Guide to the Kiln Drying of Timber. By W. C. Stevens and G. H. Pratt (FPRL, HMSO, 1961)

Kiln Drying Schedules. FPRL leaflet No. 42 (HMSO, 1959)

The Treatment of Timber in a Drying Kiln. FPRL leaflet No. 20 (HMSO, 1957)

The Air-Seasoning of Sawn Timber. FPRL leaflet No. 21 (HMSO, 1964)

The Movement of Timbers. FPRL leaflet No. 47 (HMSO, 1967)

Strength and Bending Properties

The Strength Properties of Timbers. By G. M. Lavers. FPRL bulletin No. 50 (HMSO, 1969)

The Strength of Timber. FPRL leaflet No. 55 (HMSO, 1966)

The Steam-Bending Properties of Various Timbers. FPRL leaflet No. 45 (HMSO, 1967)

Durability and Preservative Treatment

Decay of Timber and its Prevention. By K. St. G. Cartwright and W. P. K. Findlay (FPRL, HMSO, 1958)

Insect and Marine Borer Damage to Timber and Woodwork. By J. D. Bletchly (FPRL, HMSO, 1967)

(Literature references continued)

The Natural Durability of Timber. FPR record No. 30 (HMSO, 1959)
Non-pressure Methods of Applying Wood Preservatives. FPR record No. 31
    (HMSO, 1961)
The Preservative Treatment of Timber by Brushing, Spraying and Immersion. FPRL
    leaflet No. 53 (HMSO, 1962)

Working and Finishing Properties
A Handbook of Woodcutting. By P. Harris (FPRL, HMSO, 1946)
Machining and Surface Finish. FPRL technical note No. 5 (HMSO, 1966)

Uses
Wood in Building for Purposes Other Than Structural Work and Carcassing.
    (Timber Research and Development Association, 1963)
The Design and Practice of Joinery. By J. Eastwick-Field and J. Stillman
    (Architectural Press, London, 1966)
Wood Flooring (TRADA, 1959)
Wood Floors (TRADA, 1959)
Timbers for Flooring. FPR bulletin No. 40 (HMSO, 1957)
Hardwoods for Industrial Flooring. FPR Laboratory leaflet No. 48 (HMSO, 1954)
Timbers used in the Musical Instruments Industry (FPRL, 1956)
Timbers used in the Building and Repair of Railway Rolling Stock (FPRL, HMSO,
    1956)
Timbers used in the Sports Goods Industry (FPRL, HMSO, 1957)
Timbers used in Cooperage and the Manufacture of Vats and Filter Presses
    (FPRL, HMSO, 1958)
Timbers used in Motor Vehicles (FPRL, HMSO, 1958)
Timbers used in the Boat Building Industry (FPRL, HMSO, 1964)
Timbers and Board Materials used in the Furniture Industry (FPRL, HMSO, 1966)

Index

Contents of World Timbers Volume 1

Contents of World Timbers Volume 2

This book is set in the Univers series and
printed in Great Britain by
The Journal Press (W. & H. Smith Ltd.)
Evesham, Worcestershire